The
Fitness For Golfers
Handbook

Taking Your Golf Game
to the
NEXT LEVEL

**Look Better,
Feel Better,
Play A Stronger Game of Golf!**

DON TINDER
Professional Fitness Trainer for Golfers

New Century Publishers 2000

60 Bullock Drive
Unit 6
Markham, ON L3P 3P2
(905) 471-5711

US Division
P.O. Box 36
East Canaan, CT 06024
(860) 824-5301

ISBN 0-9701110-1-0

It is recommended that before beginning this or any exercise program, individuals should seek advice from their physician or a certified exercise professional. The exercises, suggestions, and ideas in this book are not intended to be a substitute for the medical advice of a trained health professional. All matters regarding your health require medical supervision. Consult your physician before adopting the suggestions in this book, as well as about any condition that may require diagnosis or medical attention. If you feel any pain or discomfort while performing the exercises or techniques in this book, stop immediately and consult your physician. The author and/or publisher cannot be held responsible for any injury or other conditions arising from following the advice or tips in this book.

Library of Congress Catalog Card Number: 00-132926

PRINTED AND BOUND IN CANADA

For additional copies, call
(877) 742-7078

To contact Don Tinder:
www.fitnessforgolfers.com

Foreword

"I have always felt for every player to reach their highest level, one must understand physical conditioning.

Many players seek improved swing motions, and are always tweaking their mechanics, yet their bodies are not capable of making the swing adjustments.

Simply, an efficient repeating swing can only be consistent with a functional body.

Strengthening and flexibility are always considered factors when one takes a lesson from me.

Don's tips will be valuable to all levels of players, and I am glad this book is available to all."

-Rick Smith
Master PGA Teaching Professional

Table of Contents

Table of Contents

For my wife, Cindy
and our beautiful blessing, Brittany

Acknowledgements

First and foremost, I would like to thank God for His countless blessings and for giving me an opportunity to spread the good news about fitness training to golfers everywhere.

I would like to thank my wife Cynthia, whose love, support, patience and assistance were invaluable to the completion of this book; my mother, Linda Tinder, my grandfather, Donald Horton, and my father-in-law, Murray Yates. Their support and encouragement meant so very much.

I've spent long hours in researching and writing this book, and this it would not have been possible were it not for the assistance of many talented people. These people contributed to important ideas, concepts, and concerns, and helped me to write this handbook from a golfer's perspective.

I would like to thank the following professional golfers who kindly contributed their opinions and ideas to this handbook: Rick Smith, Butch Harmon, Sam Snead, David Leadbetter, Jim Flick, Lee Janzen, Michelle McGann, Nancy Lopez, Brad Faxon, Bernard Langer, and Robert Damron. Thanks also goes to Pamela Smith and Criswell Freeman, whose contribution of material to this book helped to make it informative and inspiring.

Tony Smothers has been a great friend and has given me countless hours of advice and inspiration for this book. Rummel Wagner put in long hours of work and helped me in many ways. Joel Andres, M.D., lent his impressive editorial talents to this project, and I am truly grateful to him. I would like to thank Gary and Tina Brandel, and Phil and Dawn Tinder for their kind assistance.

Thanks to the following people who helped make this book a reality: Randy Myers and Steve Egan.

I would also like to thank Lifesports Health Club and Winter Pines Country Club for graciously allowing me to take photographs at their facilities.

About the Author

As an internationally published fitness consultant, writer, and fitness professional, Don Tinder has written numerous articles for magazines such as *Golf Digest, Golf Magazine, Golf Illustrated, Gentlemen's Quarterly Active, IDEA Health & Fitness Source, MuscleMag International,* and many others. His articles on current fitness topics are featured on web sites originating from a number of countries around the world, including: the U.S., France, Canada, Argentina, South Africa and China, to name a few. He is currently working on a soon-to-be-released book that takes an in-depth look at the benefits of weight resistance training for golfers.

Don's background in health and fitness spans nearly 20 years. He is a former competitive bodybuilder and semi-professional baseball player, and has been an accomplished athlete throughout his life. Don is also a highly competitive golfer and truly loves the game of golf.

A graduate of The University of Florida, he began writing about golfing fitness in early 1996. Drawing from his experience as a golfer, baseball player, and bodybuilder, Don focused on the combination of flexibility, cardiovascular, and strength training to create a golf fitness program for his fitness clients. That became the impetus for this book.

As a fitness professional, Don enjoys helping golfers achieve their fitness and golfing goals. As he has seen the countless benefits of fitness training in the sport of golf, he has thoroughly enjoyed sharing this information with readers around the world. His work has been widely accepted and highly regarded as both informative and inspiring by readers of all ages.

Don resides in Orlando, Florida with wife Cynthia and daughter, Brittany.

INTRODUCTION:
Your First Step Up to the Next Level!

"No matter how talented a player is, they will never reach their true potential unless they are willing to take the necessary time to stay physically fit."

- Butch Harmon
Instructor to Tiger Woods

As professional and amateur golfers are finally beginning to incorporate fitness into their preparation routines, millions of new golfers who start playing this great game every year are realizing that there is more to being a good golfer than meets the eye. Playing golf at a consistently high level requires mental discipline, physical control, diligent practice and consistent preparation. In order to reach your highest level of golfing performance, you must include **exercise** as preparation for practice and play.

Regular exercise (especially weight training) was once thought to produce stiff, inflexible muscles that would eventually ruin a golfer's swing. Today, professional golfers like Tiger Woods are improving their fitness, and the results are clearly evident out on the golf course. The pros realize that committing themselves to staying fit helps to maintain their high energy levels for a consistent repetitive swing, adds confidence, and improves their ability to remain focused throughout an entire round of golf.

Taking the time to stay in good physical condition provides an advantage that is as real as that five iron you hold in your hands. In fact, the countless benefits go even beyond the fairways. A renewed sense of motivation commonly is seen among those who exercise. This attitude then carries over into your play on the golf course and into your daily life.

This book will guide you through the practical steps by which you can attain a higher level of physical condition. You will learn the why, how, when, where, and what to do to get and stay in better shape.

Indeed, you are about to embark on an exciting journey; one that is both challenging and rewarding. In reading this book, you are taking that all-important first step toward the NEXT LEVEL of better golf and improved health and fitness. You'll be pleasantly surprised how relatively small amounts of time and effort will yield outstanding results in your golf game.

Chapter One starts off by giving you some inspiration! This is provided by some of the game's greatest players and instructors. These professionals are living examples of the benefits of a regular program of exercise. As you read through their testimonials, let their words inspire you to take the first step toward a new mind and body.

Chapter Two will emphasize the importance of staying motivated and committed to your fitness and golf performance goals. I will show you how to establish and maintain certain techniques and guidelines that will give you the advantage over your competition, which in many cases is **you.**

Chapter Three describes some "self-tests" that can easily be performed to determine your overall level of flexibility and strength. Once you have become aware of your physical strengths, limitations, and weaknesses, you can then target those areas with specific flexibility and strength exercises.

Chapter Four *illustrates the exercises that will assist you in increasing your level of flexibility throughout your body.* When it comes to achieving an effective golf swing, flexibility is often the most important aspect of a golfers physical condition. Flexibility allows the golfer to achieve a complete backswing and extended follow-through. In addition, increasing your flexibility not only improves the swing, but will reduce your chance of golfing injury. The most important areas of the golfer's body are targeted to improve flexibility and range-of-motion.

Chapter Five *teaches you fundamental strength training exercises.* An often overlooked element of a successful golf swing, good muscular strength is required to play with consistency and power. I will describe simple exercises that will immediately make a difference. Your ability to control your swing often comes down to your level of strength and how consistent that strength can be maintained for the <u>entire round</u>.

Chapter Six *will define cardiovascular (aerobic) training and give you the tools to incorporate this training into your daily life.* As a golfer becomes more aerobically fit, he or she has an increased ability to maintain a higher energy level for longer periods. This provides immeasurable benefits to the golfer. As world-renowned instructor David Leadbetter says, "Being tired coming down the last few holes can lead to letting a few shots slip away."

Chapter Seven *will help you learn more about golfing nutrition.* Nutrition plays a critical role in providing energy and stabilizing that energy. I will discuss some key nutritional tips and provide healthy foods and recipes that can turn your body into an energy producing machine.

Chapter Eight will enlighten you about the important topic of injury prevention. Many golfers suffer injury, in fact, almost half of all golfers report suffering an injury in their playing careers. This can be prevented through physical conditioning, good posture, and proper body mechanics. After reading this chapter, you will be more aware of what to do to prevent nagging injuries.

Chapter Nine takes your exercise routine to the golf course. Simple, effective exercises are given to help you play a better game of golf. They can be done before, during, or even after your round. Before a round, they provide you with improved flexibility and better range-of-motion. During the round, they improve blood flow and muscular feedback for better control. And after the round, the exercises help to cool down the body and protect against soreness and injury.

In summary, this book will provide you with the tools to become a better golfer. You will learn the importance of being committed to fitness, simple self-tests to determine your level of flexibility and strength, specific exercises to help you achieve a more effective swing, and concepts about muscular strength to enable your golf swing to be more consistent and powerful. In addition, this book will teach you about the important topics of cardiovascular training, golfing nutrition, and injury prevention.

As the sport of golf grows steadily in popularity each year, millions of golfers seek the tools that can help them play their very best. Unfortunately, many golfers still underestimate the physical demands placed upon them during an average round of golf. It's not enough to just take a few swings on the practice tee, make a few putts on the practice green, and expect to play at your highest level.

When a golfer becomes better conditioned by learning to exercise properly, the ability to maintain a good swing and general stamina for the entire round is improved. This, in turn, will heighten your level of confidence.

As a personal fitness trainer, I enjoy promoting fitness in my clients and people all over the world. My purpose in writing this book is to help YOU receive the many benefits of fitness training.

It's going to happen, just give it a little time. Soon, you will be spreading the word about fitness for golf. Join the countless number of new golfers playing this game every year who have discovered the "secret" of getting in shape for golf. You'll be surprised and delighted as your golf game soars to the next level! Best of luck!

-Don Tinder
March 1998

CHAPTER One

What Are the Pros Saying?
Professional Golfers Talk About the Role of Fitness in Golf.

"If there is a fountain of youth, it has to be exercise."

-Gary Player

How many times have you watched your favorite golfer smash a drive straight down the fairway or sink an impossible putt on the 18th hole to win a championship? It's inspiring to watch these pros play with such seemingly effortless skill and finesse. Ever wonder how they stay so consistent, hole after challenging hole?

One major reason is many professional golfers are taking the time to stay physically fit. Pros like Tiger Woods, Hale Irwin, Tom Kite, Gary Player, Davis Love III, Ernie Els, Nancy Lopez, Michelle McGann, to name but a few, maintain a regular exercise regimen to give themselves the competitive edge and to play at their very best. Along with instruction and practice, many of these pros are incorporating stretching, strengthening, aerobics, and good nutrition into their golfing preparation. In fact, many golfers are making fitness a daily part of their lives! Among the many benefits, these professionals know that regular exercise can:

1) enhance strength and flexibility,
2) increase energy and endurance,
3) improve consistency and control
4) increase self-confidence
5) reduce the chance for injury,
        and, let's not forget —
6) improve muscle tone and weight control.

1

Unfortunately, the thought of regular exercise is still looked upon with considerable skepticism and fear by some golfers. "Golf isn't like other sports," they may think to themselves. They worry that their swing will be negatively affected by exercising. The fear of having tight, inflexible muscles and losing precious body control cloud the minds of many of these would-be exercisers. However, here's the good news -exercise works!

Take it from the pros...

In the pages that follow, some of golf's top players and instructors give their views on the role of fitness in golf. They represent just a small sample of what countless numbers of other golfers do these days -

Get fit to play great golf!

As you read through their comments, let their words inspire you. Let them motivate you to take that first step UP to the next level!

"My experience as an instructor and coach to some of the greatest players in golf history has demonstrated to me that no matter how talented a player is, they will never reach their true potential unless they are willing to take the necessary time to stay physically fit. Golf is like many other sports that require the athlete to be in top condition BEFORE they play, not just when they perform poorly or suffer injury."

-Butch Harmon
*Instructor to **Tiger Woods***

2

"In the future, fitness is going to play a big part in golf. As a teacher, I believe in the holistic approach - golfing technique, fitness, mental (preparation), and nutrition. I utilize it for the average golfer and touring pro as well - cardiovascular training, strength, and especially flexibility. I think fitness plays an important part in mental discipline - being tired coming down the last few holes can lead to letting a few shots slip away. I think players who feel fit feel that they have the edge. I'm a big believer in fitness, and if golfers take the time to stay fit they can reach their goals."

-David Leadbetter
Instructor to Greg Norman

"Ever since turning pro in 1935, I have always been concerned with staying in shape. I watched what I ate during tournament play. I never drank alcohol or stayed up late partying - always to bed early, doing exercises consisting of sit-ups, push-ups, bicep curls and across the chest stretches before turning in. I did the same routine upon getting up in the morning. During the majority of my career on tour, we played 36 holes on Sundays, and this is one reason the guys on tour during my era were what you call "Flat Bellies" today. It took much physical and mental sharpness to finish 36 holes the last day. You cannot perform well and endure if you do not stay fit."

-The Legendary Sam Snead

"Through my exposure to Mr. Mike Malaska of Salt Lake City, Utah, our Nicklaus/Flick schools have strongly used stretching and strengthening as a significant part of our program in helping a golfer be able to put his or her body in condition to make the swing changes that he or she needs to become a better player. We have found in the past that

3

tension and the inability to have one's body react to the use of the club has significantly reduced the ability to swing the club as freely as we would like. Therefore, stretching is a very significant part of lengthening your golf career and playing more efficiently at every age. We also feel that diet and hydration (drinking plenty of water) is a factor in sustaining concentration, strength, and flexibility during the round."

-Jim Flick
*Instructor to **Tom Lehman***

"All the working out makes me more flexible, and I can play golf without getting so tired. Incorporating fitness into my golf preparation has really taken my game to the next level. I recommend that any golfer who wants to improve their game should make fitness a priority in order to play their best golf!"

-Nancy Lopez
Golfing Legend

"I think in golf it's very important to be flexible, and having flexibility and strength is better than not having it. I stretch every morning and every evening. I've had a lot of back trouble over the last 20 years, and stretching has helped me tremendously. I do cardiovascular work — riding a bike, treadmill, stairmaster. I think it helps to bring your heart rate down so you can walk fast on the golf course without being out of breath. When you're in shape I think you can focus better, concentrate better, and you don't get as tired as quickly."

-Bernard Langer
*1985, 1993 **Masters Champion***

"I'm going to train and work out even if I don't play golf because I wanna be in good shape and feel good. In golf, you have to have a combination of strength, flexibility, quickness and speed. If you are in good shape, you're physically and mentally going to last longer, and I think feeling better helps me play better."

-Brad Faxon
PGA Champion

"I have to include fitness training in my practice to keep up my stamina. Because of my medical condition, proper nutrition is also vital. Working out has helped me improve my stamina and strength. I can practice longer and maintain my busy schedule when I'm fit and in great condition."

-Michelle McGann
LPGA Star

"I think 9 out of every 10 players on tour is into some sort of fitness. The myth 10 or 15 years ago was that heavy weightlifting was bad for your swing, that you got too tight, but I think most guys lift a lot of weights. For one thing, it prevents injuries — you get stronger and you use less energy and power to hit the same shot you did before you got stronger. When you are in a steady fitness program you want to stay in shape so you eat better. I think it's a combination of being healthier, more fit, and stronger. If you're healthier you can focus better. It's going to lead to longer and better careers."

-Lee Janzen
1993, 1998 **U.S. Open Champion**

"At my age, I'm concerned with being on the tour until I'm 50 and then going on to the Senior Tour. You've got to steer away from injuries, and to be cardiovascularly fit is definitely huge, especially coming down the stretch (last few holes of a round). Stretching prevents injuries so I can stay out here forever."

-Robert Damron
PGA Champion

"I have always felt for every player to reach their highest level, one must understand physical conditioning. Many players seek improved swing motions, and are always tweaking their mechanics, yet their bodies are not capable of making the swing adjustments. Simply, an efficient repeating swing can only be consistent with a functional body. Strengthening and flexibility are always considered factors when one takes a lesson from me. "

-Rick Smith
Master PGA Tour Instructor

As you read through this handbook, think about your golf-related and fitness-related goals. What area of your golf game needs improvement? Do you need more consistency, power, control, energy, flexibility? Remember what these pros are saying about staying fit. They know it works for them — and it can work for you!

Do you want to better your scores, and have even more fun and success on the golf course? If so, then it's time to make exercise a daily part of your golf preparation. Use the techniques outlined in this handbook, have fun, and get ready to take your game to the next level!

"Practice puts your brain in your muscles."
-Sam Snead

CHAPTER Two

Motivation
Getting At What Drives You!

"Great champions have an enormous sense of pride.
The people who excel are those who are driven to
show the world—and to prove to themselves—just how
good they are."

- Nancy Lopez

Ask yourself this question, "Why do I enjoy playing golf?" Think about it for a few moments. Do you enjoy the challenge of competing with yourself? Testing your skill? The camaraderie with others? The love of the outdoors?

Whatever your reasons for enjoying this game, they give you the incentive you need to spend your afternoons and weekends out on the golf course. In other words, they provide you with the motivation to golf.

Now ask yourself another question, "What would make me want to exercise regularly?" or if you are already exercising, ask yourself, "What keeps me faithful to my workouts?"

Is it the fact that a few simple exercises can increase your ability to play golf with more energy, strength, flexibility and confidence than ever before?

Is it the short-term benefit of having more energy and reducing stress?

Is it the longer-term benefit of knowing that regular exercise helps you lose unwanted body fat, lowers your blood pressure, or any number of other long-term health benefits?

Review your responses to these two questions. Think

about your reasons for playing golf and exercising. If you take the time to consider why you play golf, you'll begin to understand the factors that motivate you to play. The same holds true for exercising. If you consider the many essential reasons for taking the time to stay fit, you'll begin to realize the importance of making the commitment to regular exercise.

Just the simple fact that you are reading this book shows a willingness to take the necessary steps to achieve your goals. You are on the right track, you've taken the first step. I congratulate you! Now it's just a matter of staying "on course" and following the techniques and the **keys to motivation** that I have outlined in this chapter and throughout this book. As you learn and apply these concepts, you will be empowered to take the steps toward ultimate success, and you'll see some exciting results as your golf game and fitness soar to the next level!

Keys to Motivation:

1. *Make the DECISION to improve your golfing fitness*
2. *Stay COMMITTED to your goals*
3. *Create a VISION of what you want to achieve*
4. *RECORD your progress*
5. *RENEW your goals every day*

"It's in your moments of decision that your destiny is shaped."

- Anthony Robbins

MAKING THE DECISION TO IMPROVE
YOUR GOLFING FITNESS

It sounds simple, but in order for you to get the most out of a golf fitness program, you must make a firm decision to become a better and healthier golfer.

Motivation begins in your mind, and any change from your normal routine starts with your initial decision to change. Making a conscious decision to participate in a regular program of exercise is an important first step towards playing a higher level of golf. It puts you on the path that will lead to better health and better golf.

STAY COMMITTED TO YOUR GOALS

Discovering what motivates a person to exercise has long been the study of psychologists, therapists, and researchers. Some people who begin an exercise program, determined to make it work, often lose that temporary motivation after a short period of time. On the other hand, many people are determined to exercise for a lifetime; they will complete the goals that they set out to accomplish. Why? What is their secret to fulfilling a lifelong commitment to fitness?

It can be defined in that one, powerful word-*commitment.*

As a fitness professional, I've learned that people who accomplish their health and fitness goals, despite any and all obstacles they face, are *determined* to succeed. They have a passionate desire that will not let anyone or anything stand in their way. They are *committed* to seeing the fulfillment of their dreams, whether it is on the golf course, in the gym, or in daily life. They know that the happiness that comes with reaching your dreams comes from a deep, driven desire to

9

stay "on course," and see your goals through to the very end. To be truly dedicated to reaching a particular goal, you must first ask yourself, **"Why am I committed to this goal? What are my reasons for achieving this goal?"** Keep in mind that your reasons must be strong enough to cause you to take action on them. If they aren't, chances are you won't feel the need to follow through to the end. You will then need to reevaluate those reasons or goals themselves in order to develop stronger reasons or goals.

DEVELOPING YOUR <u>GOALS CHART</u>

When you think of yourself in the future, do you picture a healthy, energetic individual, able to perform at your best both on and off the golf course? Do you see yourself playing your very best game of golf? If not, it might be because you haven't taken the time to clearly identify those goals that are most important to you. Identifying your goals, both in the short and long-term, provides you with a pathway which can be effectively followed.

However, it's not enough to simply know what your goals are. You must take the time to *write them down*. This can be achieved in the development of a goals chart. The act of writing down your goals will commit them to a "subconscious" level and make you more committed to achieving them. You must **1) record both your short-term and long-term goals, 2) state why you are committed to each goal, 3) identify in what time frame you wish to achieve them, and 4) establish your method for achieving each goal.**

For example, your short-term goal over a 1-2 month period may be to exercise 3 days a week by walking, stretching, and lifting light weights. Your long-term goal over a 3-6 month period may be to lose 20 pounds and lower your blood pressure by exercising regularly and eating right. *(A sample goal chart is provided in Appendix A. Your goals may or may not be similar to the ones I have listed).* It is important to keep your goals both realistic and achievable. For example, losing 20 pounds and adding 40 yards to your driving distance in one month is an unrealistic goal, especially due to the fact that you should lose no more than 1-2 lb. per week. A more realistic goal would be to lose 5 pounds and add 20 yards to your driving distance in a month. Remember, as it is in golf, patience is a virtue. Any changes that are made too quickly often do not last. You should progress at a slow, consistent, and productive pace.

Remember to record <u>all</u> of the most important goals that you are committed to reaching. As new goals are established, add them to your goals chart. It's also a good idea to choose a person to be accountable to, such as a family member, friend, or even your teaching professional. Let them know what your goals are. They can help you when you feel unmotivated. This is particularly helpful for meeting your short-term goals, which are the "stepping stones" to more permanent, long-term goals.

Expect the occasional interruptions in your fitness training such as illness, vacations, or work and family commitments. Don't worry if you have to take time off from your training. Stay committed to your short and long term goals. Before you know it, you'll gradually be back on track.

It's important to remember that when you are new to an exercise program, *simply taking the initiative to begin exercising is a significant accomplishment!* You should feel pride in making this new, positive change in your life.

CREATING A VISION

Once you have decided what your specific goals are, it's time to create your vision. In golf, you should envision your next shot going exactly where you want it to go, even before you swing at the ball. It's the same with your fitness goals - your ultimate success in achieving your fitness goals comes down to your ability to *clearly picture yourself achieving them.*

This process of creating a vision of achieving your goals, before you actually achieve them, will form the direct pathway for those goals to be realized. It's also important to rehearse your goals *in detail,* seeing yourself as already having achieved exactly what you envision, with complete confidence.

In his book, *First Things First,* best-selling author and motivational expert Stephen Covey states:

"Vision is the best manifestation of creative imagination and the primary motivation of human action. It's the ability to see beyond our present reality, to create, to invent what does not yet exist, to become what we not yet are."

If your goal is to play golf at the next level, creating a vision of a healthy, energetic, skilled player is a crucial step in realizing that goal.

Be *passionate* about your vision. Don't concern yourself with where you are now, at this moment. Instead, create a positive vision of the future. Perhaps one of your goals is to add 30, 40, or 50 yards to your driving distance. If so, then clearly picture yourself doing it.

Imagine standing at the first tee, with your body in better shape than ever before. Picture yourself holding a driver confidently in your hands and addressing the ball. Imagine your friends watching as you make a smooth backswing, then hitting the ball, sending it farther and straighter down the center of the fairway than ever before!

Can you picture this in your mind? Try this for yourself, using one of your goals. As you become better at creating a positive image in your mind's eye, your motivation and ultimate ability to achieve those goals will be stronger than ever before. *Take the time to do this every day!* The process of creating a vision of what you want to achieve, both in your fitness and golf game, sets the stage for ultimate success!

RECORD YOUR PROGRESS

I know what you're thinking. You don't even want to think about taking the time to *write things down.* It's just too much trouble. But, believe me when I tell you, IT WORKS! I have seen it happen with many of my clients.

As you begin your exercise program, become aware of your attitudes, feelings and emotions. Keep track of them by writing them down in a training journal. Recording your actions and thoughts in a journal can provide valuable feedback to help keep you aware of your mental state and remain motivated by giving you a clear picture of your overall progress *(in Appendix C, I have provided a sample exercise journal that you may copy or enlarge, or use as a guide in developing your own journal).*

Be sure that your journal includes your *exercises performed, golf performance, golf scores, and related thoughts about your exercise experience (both positive and negative)*. Remember, the more detail you can provide on specific exercises performed and your related thoughts and attitude, the greater your ability to analyze your overall progress and make any necessary improvements.

In addition, at the end of each week, observe how you felt about your fitness training and overall golf performance. What did you feel were the positive aspects of the week? What were the negative aspects? Write them down. Doing so will keep you focused on your original goals and motivate you to achieve them.

Use a calendar or planner (something you refer to often) to schedule your exercise sessions in advance. You will be less likely to skip a workout if you plan ahead. As you will see as you read the upcoming chapters on specific exercises and routines, your golf fitness program can be performed almost anywhere, so don't worry if you're on the road or away from a gym or golf course.

Plan ahead for your exercise sessions according to your particular schedule, but make your fitness time a top priority. Doing so will help to keep you motivated, energized, and will dramatically increase your chances for success on (and off!) the golf course.

RENEW YOUR GOALS EVERY DAY

Remember to update your goals on a daily basis. Each day, confidently renew your commitment to each one of your goals. You may do this verbally or write it down and keep it with you throughout the day. Taking the time to do this will give you the added strength and determination to make it through those tougher days, as well as reinforce your efforts to achieve each of your goals.

Remember that each day will present its own challenges and rewards. Take each new day as it comes and give it your best effort. Stay focused on your goals and you will reach them! It only takes a little time. Remember, *every journey begins with a single step!*

"You are what you <u>think</u> you are, in golf and in life."
                                        -Raymond Floyd

15

CHAPTER Three

Golf Fitness Assessment
Turning Your Weaknesses Into Strengths!

"Most golfers prepare for disaster, a good golfer
prepares for success."

-Bob Toski

Before you embark on the rewarding journey toward a healthier body and a better golf game, you should take the time to *evaluate* your present level of fitness; specifically, your level of *flexibility* and *strength*. Assessing your levels of flexibility and strength will help you to identify any physical limitations or weaknesses you may have in these two areas. These limitations and weaknesses can have a negative impact on your ability to play your best golf.

The self-tests described in this chapter allow you to evaluate your:

- flexibility
- range of motion, and
- strength

in the muscles, joints, and connective tissues involved in a typical golf swing. These three elements (flexibility, range of motion, strength) play ·a major role in achieving and maintaining a consistently effective golf swing.

After you determine what parts of your body are weak or inflexible, you can then perform effective stretching and strengthening exercises that target those weaker areas.

Stretching and strengthening your weaker areas will result in increased flexibility, range of motion, and overall strength.

As you perform these self-tests, pay attention to areas of your body that have low (listed as "fair" or "below average") flexibility or strength. Dedicate yourself to improving those areas (reaching the "good" or "excellent" level) by performing the **<u>suggested exercise</u>** (described at the end of each self-test section) **every other day, or at least 3 times a week.** You may perform the tests and suggested exercises at home, on the road, or in the gym. Remember to hold each **stretch for a minimum to 15-20 seconds** to adequately improve flexibility of weaker areas and to achieve optimum results.

In addition, along with the suggested exercises, **optional exercises** are given for each self-test. These can be performed for even greater improvement **(descriptions for these optional exercises can be found in Chapters 4 & 5).** Although you can achieve good results by performing only the suggested exercises, I recommend that you also incorporate the two optional exercises from each section into your stretching and strengthening exercises. If your goal is to improve a weaker area of your body in the shortest amount of time, adding the optional exercises to your overall routine will ensure complete and efficient results.

These exercises are designed to enhance efficiency of movement in key areas of the body. To evaluate your progress periodically, perform the flexibility and strength self-tests every 4-6 weeks to measure your overall improvement.

Self-Test Guidelines

A few guidelines should be followed when performing the tests of flexibility:
- Do not bounce or strain; perform the tests slowly and carefully. This leads to better results and can help you to avoid any unnecessary injury.
- Warm up for 3-5 minutes before performing these tests (for example; walking in place, riding a stationary bike, etc.). This promotes the flow of blood and increases the temperature of involved muscles and tissues.
- Except where otherwise noted, both women and men may use the same scale for interpreting test results.

Part I:
Flexibility

A word of caution: These flexibility and strength tests are designed to measure flexibility and strength in otherwise healthy individuals. Those who find the tests too difficult to perform and/or have a history of severe or chronic muscle or joint inflexibility should seek attention from a qualified physical therapist or sports medicine specialist. He or she can determine any specific areas of weakness or limitation, assist you in becoming more aware of your particular golfing fitness needs, and provide you with a prescribed routine of specialized treatment.

Many golfers tend to exhibit chronic tightness in the following areas of their body:

⇨ **lower back**
⇨ **front and back of the thighs**
⇨ **hips**
⇨ **front shoulders**
⇨ **chest**
⇨ **neck**

It's very important to stretch these "golfing muscles" on a regular basis, particularly if you experience chronic tightness or limited range of motion in your golf swing.

Self-test #1:
Lower Back (forward bending)

Being able to comfortably bend forward from the waist and lower back is critical in maintaining balance in your setup and provide needed power and control throughout your swing. This test will measure flexibility in your trunk (lower back, hips, and hamstrings).
Setup: You'll need a yardstick and some masking tape for this one. Sit on the floor on a mat or padded surface with your legs straight and feet approximately 12 inches apart. Place the tape on the floor and line up your heels with the tape. Place the yardstick in between your legs, with the 12 inch mark of the yardstick lined up at the point where your heels meet the tape.

> Your trunk should be able to move forward onto your thighs, with the motion occurring at the hips and lower back, not the upper back or neck.

Movement Performance: Place one hand on top of your other with your fingers aligned. Exhale, and slowly lean forward by dropping the head toward the arms, keeping your knees straight and your fingers in contact with the yardstick. Reach for the farthest point on the yardstick. Repeat 3 times and average the results for all 3 attempts.

Interpreting Your Results:
Excellent - 15 inch mark or more on the ruler.
Good - 12-15 inch mark.
Fair - 8-12 inch mark.
Below Average - Less than 8 inch mark.

Note: Because women generally tend to be more flexible, add 3 inches to the numbers shown above. For example, excellent forward-bending flexibility for women is the 18 inch mark or above.

Suggested Exercise for Test #1:
Seated Hamstring Stretch

Target Area: This exercise targets the muscles of the hamstrings and lower back.

Movement Performance: Assume a seated position. Spread your legs apart and slowly reach forward toward your right  foot until you feel a comfortable stretch in the back of the right thigh (hamstring). Try to keep your back as straight as possible (avoid excessive rounding of the back). Hold for a minimum of 15-20 seconds. Repeat with the other leg. Perform twice with each leg.

Optional Exercises -
• Knee Huggers (Chapter 4)
• Low Back/Hamstring Stretch (Chapter 4)

Self-test #2:
Lower Back (backward bending)

Good flexibility in your lower back helps to provide stability, balance, and power throughout your swing. Your ability to maintain good posture from the address position through the swing, and tolerate a slight backwards lean as you finish your swing depends largely on your flexibility as you extend your lower back (bend backwards).

Setup: Lie face down on a mat or padded surface, with your hands in a push-up position.

As in the previous test, try to bend at the hips and lower back, as opposed to the upper back or neck.

Movement Performance: Slowly push your upper body up while keeping your lower back as relaxed as possible and attempting to keep your hip bones in contact with the floor.

Interpreting Your Results:
Excellent - Your hips remain in contact with floor when your arms are fully straight.
Good - Your hips rise off the floor one inch when your arms are fully straight.
Fair - Your hips rise off the floor two inches when your arms are straight.

Below Average - Your hips rise more than two inches off the floor when your arms are straight.

Suggested Exercise for Test #2:
Standing Hip Flexor Stretch
Target Area:
Front of the
hips and thighs.

Movement Performance: Stand with the right leg approximately 3 feet behind the left leg, with legs shoulder width apart. Make sure that the left knee is directly over the left foot and ankle. The rear leg should be just slightly bent with the weight of that leg placed on the balls of the foot. Exhale as you slowly bend your left leg and press your hips downward toward the floor until a comfortable stretch is felt in the right front hip area. Hold for a minimum of 15-20 seconds. Repeat with the other side, 2 times each side.

Optional Exercises -
• Cobra Stretch (Chapter 4)
• Standing or Seated Back Arch (Chapter 4)

Self-test #3:
Hip flexibility (hamstrings & rear hips)

Tight hamstrings and hips can affect balance and good swing mechanics, and put unnecessary pressure on your lower back, increasing the risk of injury to that area.

Setup: You need a towel for this one. Lie on your back on a mat or padded surface. Wrap a towel around the back of your right thigh, near the knee. Keep your left leg firmly pressed into the floor.

Movement Performance: Use the towel and attempt to pull your right leg upwards to an angle as close to 80 to 85 degrees as possible. Remember to keep the right leg straight and do not raise it past the point of comfort (there should be no pain in the back of the right thigh). Repeat with the other leg.

> Do not bend at the knee or raise your leg to the point of pain in the back of your thigh.

Interpreting Your Results:
Excellent - Your leg raises to an angle of 80 degrees or more.
Good - Your leg raises to an angle of 70-80 degrees.
Fair - Your leg raises to an angle of 60-70 degrees.
Below Average - Your leg raises less than 60 degrees.

Suggested Exercise for Test #3:
Lying Hamstring Stretch
Target Area: Hamstrings.

Movement Performance: This exercise is simply test #3; however, it is performed for flexibility improvement. Lie on your back on a mat or padded surface. Wrap a towel around the back of your right thigh, near the knee. Keeping your left leg firmly pressed into the floor, use the towel to pull your right leg upwards to an angle as close to vertical as possible. Exhale as you lift the leg. Remember to keep the right leg straight and do not raise it past the point of comfort (there should be no pain in the back of the right thigh). Hold for a minimum of 15-20 seconds. Repeat with the other leg for a total of 2-3 times with each leg.

Optional Exercises -
• Seated Hamstring Stretch (Chapter 4)
• Low Back/Hamstring Stretch (Chapter 4)

Self-test #4:
Hip flexibility (hip flexors)

    Tight hip flexor muscles in the front of your hips can place serious stress on your lower back muscles and lumbar spine, while flexible hip flexors will help to keep your lower back pain-free and contribute to good posture and balance throughout your swing.
Setup: Lie on your back on a mat or padded surface.

It's important to try to keep your lower leg flat on the floor. This will help to reveal any tightness in the front hip of that leg.

Movement Performance: Grasp your right leg behind the knee and pull that leg toward your chest. Attempt to keep your left leg pressed firmly into the floor. Repeat with the other leg.

Interpreting Your Results:
Excellent - Your lower leg remains flat on the floor and does not raise up at all.
Good - Your lower leg raises slightly (an inch or less).
Fair - Your lower leg raises moderately (1-2 inches).
Below Average - Your lower leg raises severely (over 2 inches off the floor).

Suggested Exercise for Test #4:
Cobra Stretch
Target Area: Lower back, hips, stomach.

Movement Performance: Lie on your stomach on a comfortable surface. Place your hands at push-up position at just below shoulder level, fingers pointing forward. Exhale as you push your upper body upwards, gently arching your back until a stretch is felt in the stomach and lower back. Try to keep your hip bones in contact with the floor at all times. Hold for a minimum of 15-20 seconds. Repeat 3 times. Note: If you cannot achieve a straight-arm position, you may rest on your elbows as pictured on next page.

Optional Exercises -

• Standing Hip Flexor Stretch (Chapter 4)
• Leaning Hip Flexor Stretch (Chapter 4)

Self-test #5:
Shoulder flexibility (shoulder rotation)

The shoulders play a very active role in the golf swing. The rotator cuff muscles (located in the upper back, near the shoulders) are responsible for rotating the shoulders and lifting the arms during the take-away and follow-through in your swing. Flexible muscles in these areas will help to keep your shoulders injury-free and improve your range of motion.

Setup: Perform this test either standing or seated.

This test measures shoulder rotation - which is key to a good take-away and follow through in your swing.

Movement Performance: Extend your right arm up and bend at your elbow until the right hand comes to rest, palm down, between your shoulder blades. Reach back with your left hand, palm up, attempting to gently touch the fingers of the other hand. Repeat with the opposite arm.

Interpreting Your Results:

(You'll need a two-way mirror to see where your fingers are).

Excellent - Your fingers touch or overlap.

Good - Your fingers do not touch, but are less than an inch apart.

Fair - Your fingers are 1-2 inches apart.

Below Average - Your fingers are more than 2 inches apart.

Suggested Exercise for Test #5:
Chest Stretch
Target Area: Chest and front shoulders.

Movement Performance: While either standing or sitting in an upright position, reach your hands behind your body and clasp them together. You may also hold a golf club behind you with your palms facing up:

Raise your arms and stick your chest out, while moving your elbows and shoulder blades back. Inhale deeply to fully stretch the chest. Hold for a minimum of 15-20 seconds. Repeat 3 times.

Optional Exercises -
• Triceps Stretch (Chapter 4)
• Doorway Stretch (Chapter 4)

Self-test #6:
Shoulder flexibility (adductor flexibility)

Many golfers are tight in their front shoulders (adductors) and chest. This can not only affect your ability to make a complete turn away from and through the ball, but also contributes to poor golfing posture. Over time, this can result in chronically poor posture (pictured below).

This type of posture can place dangerous stress on your muscles and joints, as well as reduce your ability to maintain consistent and effective swing mechanics.

Setup: Lie on your back on a mat or padded surface. Bend at your knees, and flatten your back into the padded surface.

Flexibility in the shoulders contributes to the all-important element of good posture in your setup and swing.

Movement Performance: Keeping your back pressed down, extend your arms up and over your head toward the floor. Attempt to lay your arms down flat on the floor over your head.

Interpreting Your Results:
Excellent - Your arms lie comfortably flat on the floor over your head (as shown).
Good - Your arms are raised 2 inches or less.

Fair - Your arms are raised 2-4 inches.
Below Average - Your arms are raised 4 or more inches off the surface.

Suggested Exercise for Test #6:
Prayer Stretch

Target Area: Shoulders, upper back and chest.

Movement Performance: Bend at your knees and reach forward to place your hands, palms down and shoulder width apart on a bar or level surface, such as a tabletop (or you may assume a hands and knees position, placing your hands on a chair).

Stick your buttocks back, bend your knees and lower your head and chest toward the floor until you feel a comfortable stretch in the shoulders, upper back, and chest (if you are on your hands and knees, sink backwards until your buttocks rests on your heels, or until you feel a comfortable stretch). Exhale to deeply feel this stretch. Hold for a minimum of 15-20 seconds. Repeat 3 times.

Optional Exercises -
• Triceps Stretch (Chapter 4)
• Doorway Stretch (Chapter 4)

Part II:
Strength

These tests will measure your strength in the muscles most involved in your golf swing. Improving strength in these muscles can add power, distance, and improve your overall energy throughout a round of golf.

Self-test #1:
Chest, shoulder, triceps strength

Much of the power that is generated in your swing comes from the muscles of the chest, shoulders, and triceps. Strong muscles in these areas contribute to added power and distance in your swing.

Setup: Lie face down on a mat or padded surface and place your hands in a push-up position near your shoulders with the fingers pointing forward. Keep your back straight throughout this test.

> Don't forget to warm up and **stretch** before beginning these strength tests and exercises. The stretches given in the previous section are ideal to perform **before** attempting the strength tests and exercises.

Start

Finish

For men, use the standard push-up position with only the hands and toes in contact with the floor (as pictured previous page).

Start   **Finish**

For women, place the knees on the ground in a modified push-up position (pictured above).

Movement Performance: Keeping your back straight, exhale as you push your upper body off the floor until your arms are fully extended. Inhale as you slowly return to the starting position, making sure your chest does not come in contact with the floor (it should remain about one inch off the floor at the bottom of the movement). Keep your elbows pointed directly out to the sides throughout the exercise. Complete as many push-ups as possible until you cannot continue. Be sure to count them as you go.

Interpreting Your Results: Men -
Push-ups Performed

Age	(15-19)	(20-29)	(30-39)	(40-49)	(50-59)	(60-69)
Excellent	39 + up	36 + up	30 + up	22 + up	21 + up	18 + up
Good	29-38	29-35	22-29	17-21	13-20	11-17
Fair	18-28	17-28	12-21	10-16	7-12	5-10
Below Average	up to 18	up to 17	up to 12	up to 10	up to 7	up to 5

Interpreting Your Results: Women - Pushups Performed

Age	(15-19)	(20-29)	(30-39)	(40-49)	(50-59)	(60-69)
Excellent	33 + up	30 + up	27 + up	24 + up	21 + up	17 + up
Good	25-32	21-29	20-26	15-23	11-20	12-16
Fair	12-24	10-20	8-19	5-14	2-10	1-11
Below Average	up to 12	up to 10	up to 8	up to 5	up to 2	up to 1

Suggested Exercise for Test #1:
Push-ups
Target Area: Chest, shoulders, and triceps.

Start   **Finish**

Movement Performance: It's the same as for the test itself. Perform up to 20-30 push-ups without stopping. Rest for one minute. Repeat 3 times. Note: Women use the modified push-up version (knees remain on the floor).

It might sound simple, but one of the best exercises golfers can do for strengthening the muscles of the chest,

> Don't forget to incorporate your **stretching** exercises with the strengthening exercises. This will lead to better flexibility and strength, and will help prevent the development of tight, stiff muscles.

shoulders, and triceps is the good old push-up. As you become stronger and able to perform more of these before becoming tired, you will notice an increased ability to generate power in your swing.

Self-Test #2:
Leg strength

Strong legs contribute to a strong and stable lower body during the golf swing, allowing you to incorporate more power into your stroke and adding to your overall energy throughout an entire round of golf.

Setup: Position yourself in front of a wall with your legs shoulder width apart and feet pointed straight ahead.

Movement Performance: Rest against the wall with your upper body and proceed to sit down against the wall until your thighs are just above parallel with the floor. Keep your knees directly over your ankles. Do not allow the thighs to drop down past parallel with the floor, as this puts excess pressure on the knees.

Keep your lower back pressed into the wall and remain in a seated position as long as you possibly can. Use a watch or count to yourself to keep track of your time.

Interpreting Your Results:
Excellent - You can remain in a seated position for over 90 seconds.
Good - You remain in a seated position for 60-90 seconds.
Fair - You remain in a seated position for 30-60 seconds.
Below Average - You remain in a seated position for less than 30 seconds.

Suggested Exercise for Test #2:
The Squat

Target Area: Legs.

Start

Finish

Movement Performance: Stand with your legs shoulder width apart, knees slightly bent, and toes pointed slightly outward. Keep your body weight centered over the middle of your feet and your arms held straight out in front of you at shoulder height.

Drop your buttocks down and back until your thighs are at a point parallel with the floor. Hold for a count of one, then return to standing position. Do not lock your knees in the standing position (keep them slightly bent). Repeat 10-15 times. Rest for one minute, and repeat again for 10-15 times. (If this exercise causes discomfort in the knees, discontinue and consult your physician before attempting).

> Much of your power in the swing is derived from the leg muscles. The squat strengthens the thighs, hips, and buttocks muscles and is beneficial for maintaining a strong lower body from which to anchor your swing.

35

Optional Exercises:
• Lunges (Chapter 5)
• Squats (holding dumbbells in hands) (Chapter 5)

Self-Test #3:
Bent-knee Curl-up (abdominal strength)

Well-trained abdominal muscles enhance your ability to generate power in the rotation of your trunk as you shift your weight from side to side during the swing.

Setup: Lie on the floor on a mat or padded surface. Keep your feet flat on the floor and bend your knees to around 45 degrees. Cross your arms and place them on your chest.

Movement Performance: Slowly curl your upper body to as close to a 45 degree angle as possible (upper back should be off the floor). Maintain that position for as long as you can. Use a clock or wristwatch to keep track of your time.

Interpreting Your Results:
Excellent - Holding for 60 seconds or more.
Good - Holding for 30-60 seconds.
Fair - Holding for 10-30 seconds.
Below Average - Holding for less than 10 seconds.

Suggested Exercise for Test #3:
Abdominal Crunch

Target Area: Abdominals.

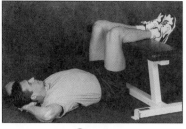

Start   **Finish**

Movement Performance: Lie on your back on a mat or padded surface with your legs bent and resting on a flat bench (or at 90 degrees as in the test above). Place your hands behind your head and keep your elbows pointed outward.

Using abdominal strength, (DO NOT PULL WITH YOUR HANDS – this can strain or aggravate the muscles of your neck and upper back) curl your shoulders and upper back up, exhaling as you go. Hold for two seconds at the peak contracted position, then slowly lower your upper back down. Repeat 10-15 times. Rest for 15 seconds. Repeat 10-15 times twice more. Work your way up to a total of 25-50 continuous repetitions without stopping.

Optional Exercises:
• Twisting Crunches (Chapter 5)
• Knee Tuck Crunches (Chapter 5)

A strong midsection provides a golfer with the ability to turn into the ball with power and helps protect the lower back from injury.

CHAPTER Four

Flexibility Training:
STRETCHING *Your Limits!*

"Fight tightness whenever it occurs; strive for relaxed muscles throughout."
-Bobby Jones

Bobby Jones was right! Tight, inflexible muscles can be a golfer's worst enemy. In order to maintain a consistently smooth and successful golf swing, you must develop good flexibility throughout the entire swing. As your flexibility and range of motion increase, your ability to perform a complete backswing and extended follow-through improves. In fact, improved flexibility leads to maximum clubhead speed at impact with the ball, and results in a more powerful, controlled, and consistent golf swing.

Muscles and tissues tend to shorten over one's lifetime; however, regular stretching and flexibility exercises can prevent and even reverse this problem. Taking the time to do a few simple stretches *every day* (especially before, during, and after your rounds of golf) helps you maintain a tension-free body, remain mentally calm and focused, and reduces your chances of injury. This leads to better golf performance.

Taking the relatively small amount of time to perform these stretches will pay off generously. You'll have more energy, greater control of your swing, and you'll be better prepared to play your best golf. And here's the best part...you'll **HAVE MORE FUN!**

Flexibility Training Benefits

1. Regular stretching will result in less overall energy needed for you to perform at higher levels. This conserves energy throughout the round and enhances your game.
2. Improves range of motion and coordination.
3. Enhances muscular feedback - helps to improve muscular control and promotes the awareness of discomfort, avoiding potential injuries.
4. Improves balance and posture - enhances the development of maximum power in your swing.
5. Increases circulation of blood and nutrients to joints and tissues.
6. Promotes muscular relaxation and reduces post-activity muscle soreness.
7. Enhances your enjoyment of golf - a conditioned, flexible golfer will perform at higher levels and maintain his or her energy for longer periods.

Stretching Guidelines

⇨ **Warm-up for 3-5 minutes** - consisting of a low intensity aerobic activity, such as walking or jogging in place, riding a stationary bike, or climbing up and down stairs a few times. This will provide the muscles and tissues with adequate blood flow and increase the temperature of those working muscles.

⇨ **Hold for a minimum of 15-20 seconds.** If the stretch is for improvement of a weak area (as determined by the self-assessment exercises in Chapter 3), hold the stretch for 30 to 60 seconds.

⇨ **Proceed slowly.** Do not jerk or bounce as you stretch. Stretch until you feel a comfortable pulling sensation. If you feel as though you could comfortably hold the stretch forever, then you are doing it correctly.

⇨ **Relax.** Breathe slowly, deeply, and comfortably. Imagine yourself playing golf while you perform your stretching exercises. This can help provide an important mind/body connection that can help you relax the next time you play.

⇨ **Stretch both sides of your body equally.** Studies have shown that both sides are equally as active during the swing.

⇨ **Be patient.** You will gradually become more flexible as you take the time to perform these exercises.

If you are not used to regular stretching, begin by performing only <u>one stretch</u> from each section on <u>three different days</u> each week. For example, choose one stretch from the following areas of your body: legs, hips, lower back, trunk, upper body, and arms (<u>six total stretches</u>).

As you gradually improve your flexibility and become accustomed to the exercises (**within 2-4 weeks of consistent stretching**), you should increase the total number of stretches to include one additional stretch for each section of the body.

After an additional 4-6 weeks of consistent regular stretching, increase the total number of stretching exercises to include all those listed in this chapter. Perform the entire series of stretches 3-5 days per week on alternate days (for example, Monday-Wednesday-Friday).

After an additional 2-4 weeks of consistently performing the entire series of stretches, you may then maintain your level of flexibility by performing the exercises on just 2-3 alternate days each week. You will begin to notice that over a short period of time these exercises will become a natural part of your regular routine. At this point, the entire flexibility routine should take between 20-30 minutes to perform, 2-3 times per week.

41

To keep your stretching routine challenging and effective, change the order (sequence) of exercises every two weeks or so.

Ask your local golf pro about ways to incorporate good form and swing mechanics that can add to your overall flexibility during play.

Finally, it's always a good idea to consult a physician and/or physical therapist to determine your limitations and specific goals in a flexibility program.

The exercises described in this chapter can be done at home, at the gym, or on the road. For most of these stretches you will need only a comfortable floor or padded mat, a towel, and about 6-10 square feet of space.

> **"Practice, which some regard as a chore, should be approached as just about the most pleasant recreation ever devised."**
> - Babe Didrikson Zaharias

LEGS

Quadriceps Stretch - Target Area: Thighs.

Standing tall, grasp your right ankle and gently pull that leg backwards and up until you feel a gentle stretch in the top of the thigh. Keep your knees pointed toward the floor. Hold 15-30 seconds. Repeat with the other leg. Do 2 times with each leg.

**Seated Hamstring Stretch -
Target Area**: Hamstrings.

In a seated position, spread your legs apart to a comfortable distance. Exhale as you slowly reach forward toward the right foot, as far as you can comfortably go. Keep your head up and avoid rounding your back. Try to feel the stretch in the hamstring area. Hold 15-30 seconds. Repeat with the left leg. Do 2 times with each leg.

**Lying Hamstring Stretch -
Target Area**: Hamstrings.

Lie on your back on a mat or padded surface. Wrap a towel around the back of your right thigh, near the knee. Keeping your left leg firmly pressed into the floor, use the towel to pull your right leg upwards to an angle as close to vertical as possible. Exhale slowly as you lift the leg. Hold 15-30 seconds.

Remember to keep the right leg as straight as possible and do not raise it past the point of comfort (there should be no pain in the back of the thigh). Repeat with the other leg for a total of 2 times with each leg.

Groin Stretch -
Target Area: Inner Thigh, Groin.

Assume a seated position. Grab your ankles and pull the feet together until the soles of the feet touch. Exhale slowly as you gently pull your heels towards your groin, while at the same time using the elbows to gently push downwards on the knees until a comfortable stretch is felt in the groin. Hold 15-30 seconds. Repeat 2 times.

Standing Calf Stretch -
Target Area: Calf Muscle

In a standing position, place your left foot 2-3 feet behind the right. Bend your right knee slightly and keep your left leg straight with the left heel pressed down to the ground. Exhale slowly and lean your hips forward until you feel a comfortable stretch in your left calf muscle. Hold 15-30 seconds. Repeat with the other leg. Do 2 times with each leg.

<u>HIPS</u>

Standing Hip Flexor Stretch -
Target Area: Front Hips.

Stand with the right leg approximately 3 feet behind the left leg, with legs shoulder-width apart. Make sure that the left knee is directly over the left foot and ankle. Exhale as you slowly press your hips downward toward the floor until a comfortable stretch is felt in the right front hip area. Hold 15-30 seconds. Repeat with the other side, 2 times each side.

Leaning Hip Flexor Stretch -
Target Area: Front Hips.

This stretch is similar to the previous one, except you will be using the aid of a bench. Stand directly along the left side of the bench. Place both hands on the front of the bench and rest your right thigh and knee on the bench while bending the left leg, keeping the left knee directly over the left foot. Exhale and press your hips downwards while keeping the chest and head up, slightly arching your back until you feel a stretch in the right hip. Hold 15-30 seconds. Repeat with other leg for a total of 2 times with each leg.

**Lying Hip Rotator Stretch -
Target Area:** Hip rotators.

Lie on your back with your legs bent to 45 degrees. Place your right ankle on your left knee. Using the right hand, exhale and gently apply pressure to the right knee until a stretch is felt in the outer right hip region. Hold 15-30 seconds. Repeat with the other leg. Repeat 2 times with each leg.

**Hip Abductor Stretch
Target Area:** Outer hips, buttocks.

In a seated, upright position, place your right foot against the outside of your left knee, keeping the left leg flat on the floor. Place your right hand behind you and, using your left hand, exhale slowly and gently pull your right knee toward your left shoulder. Try to look over your right shoulder and feel a comfortable stretch in the outer right hip area. Hold 15-30 seconds. Repeat to the opposite side. Repeat twice to each side.

LOWER BACK

**Standing or Seated Back Arch
Target Area:** Lower Back.

In a standing or seated position, assume an upright posture. Place both hands near the lower back, fingers

pointed downward. Apply light pressure downward with your hands. Inhale as you lift your chest upward and squeeze your shoulder blades together. You should feel a release of tension in the lower back.

Standing   **Seated**

Hold 15-30 seconds. Repeat twice.

Knee Huggers -
Target Area: Hips, buttocks, lower back.

Lie on your back on a comfortable surface. Keeping your back firmly pressed into the floor, exhale as you pull your knees upward and into your chest until a comfortable stretch is felt in the lower back. You can lift your head slightly to meet your knees. Hold 15-30 seconds. Repeat 2 times.

Angry Cat Stretch -
Target Area: Back

Assume a hands and knees position on the floor. Inhale as you place your chin on your chest and round your back, drawing in your stomach muscles. Hold this position for

47

Start   **Finish**

15-30 seconds, then exhale as you arch your back and pull your head up. Hold this position another 15-30 seconds. Repeat twice.

Cobra Stretch -
Target Area: Lower back, hips, stomach.

Lie on your stomach on a comfortable surface. Place your hands at a push-up position at just below shoulder level, with your fingers pointing forward. Exhale as you push your upper body upwards, gently arching your back until a stretch is felt in the stomach and lower back. Try to keep your hip bones in contact with the floor at all times. Hold 15-30 seconds. Repeat 2 times.

Low Back / Hamstring Stretch -
Target Area: Lower back, buttocks, hamstrings, calves.

With your feet shoulder width apart and toes pointed slightly outward, place your right foot about 2-2 1/2 feet in front and bend your left knee as you slowly reach toward and grasp your right toe (if you cannot reach your toe, grasp the

leg at the farthest point you can comfortably reach). Keep your chin up and exhale slowly, leaning forward until you feel a comfortable stretch in the back of the right leg, near the knee. Keep your back as straight as possible (do not round). Hold for 15-30 seconds. Repeat with the left leg. Repeat twice.

Praying Lower Back Stretch-Target Area: Lower/middle back.

Assume a hands and knees position on a mat or padded surface with your knees slightly wider than shoulder-width apart. Exhale and "press" your buttocks down and backwards in between your knees, while at the same time pushing your hands and arms away from you as your arms straighten. Allow your buttocks to travel down in between your knees until a comfortable stretch is felt in your lower and middle back region. Hold 15-30 seconds. Return to start. Repeat twice.

TRUNK

Seated Trunk Rotation -
Target Area: Side abdominals, obliques, hips, lower back.

In a seated position, keeping your pelvis stationary, rotate your body to the right and grab the back of a bench, chair, or golf cart (as shown below). Slowly exhale and try to look over

your left shoulder as you stretch, increasing tension gradually by pulling a little farther with your hands, gently increasing the effectiveness of the stretch. Hold 15-30 seconds. Repeat twice to each side. Note: If you are standing, simply back up against a stationary object such as a pole or tree.

Side Bend Stretch -
Target Area: Side muscles of your trunk, near the rib cage.

Stand with your feet shoulder width apart and left hand held directly over your head. Lean to your right side and place your right hand on or near your right knee. You may support some body weight with that hand. Exhale and continue leaning until you feel a comfortable stretch along the left side of your trunk. Hold for 15-30 seconds and repeat to the other side. Repeat twice to each side.

Trunk Flexion -
Target Area: Trunk and inner thighs.

Sit up straight on the edge of a chair (or at the edge of a golf cart as shown) with your legs spread apart and your feet flat on the ground. Tuck your chin down and slowly curl your upper body toward your thighs. Exhale and let your body

relax. You may hold this position by placing the arms behind the calves and applying light pressure to feel an additional stretch in the lower back. Hold this position for 15-30 seconds. Slowly uncurl to the starting position, bringing your head up last. Repeat twice.

Trunk Rotation with club -
Target Area: Trunk, abdominals, hips.

Standing or seated, place a golf club behind your head and shoulders. With your knees slightly bent, slowly rotate your upper body to one side, keeping your pelvis stationary and facing front, until you feel a comfortable stretch in the side abdomen. Exhale and hold for 5 seconds. Repeat to other side. Do up to five times to each side. Try to feel a gradual increase in rotation with each repetition.

Side Lying Trunk Rotation -
Target Area: Hips, lower back, sides.

Lie on the floor on your left side and place your legs at a 90 degree angle to your upper body. Place your left hand on the lower right thigh and apply light pressure. Slowly rotate your body to the right, away from the legs. Reach back with the right arm and try to touch the back of your right shoulder to the floor, but, *do not force it.* Exhale and hold for 15-30 seconds. Repeat to the other side. Repeat twice to each side.

UPPER BODY

Chest Stretch-
Target Area: Chest, shoulders.

Standing or seated, reach your hands behind you and clasp them together. Raise your arms and stick your chest out while moving your elbows and shoulders back. Attempt to touch your shoulder blades together. Inhale deeply to achieve a full stretch in the chest region. Hold 15-30 seconds.

Repeat 2 times.

Shoulder Stretch -
Target Area: Shoulders and rotator cuff muscles.

Standing or seated, reach across your body and under the right elbow, as shown. Grasp the back of your right elbow with your left hand and gently pull that arm across your body and under your chin until you feel a comfortable stretch in the shoulder region. Exhale and hold for 15-30 seconds. Repeat with the other arm. Repeat twice with each arm.

Start

Rotator Cuff Stretch -
Target Area: Rotator cuff muscles in the upper back and shoulders.

In a standing or seated position, place your knuckles against your temples as shown with your thumbs pointed down, elbows pushed back. attempt to bring your elbows together in front of you, *but don't force them together.* Keep your head stationary and your knuckles pressed against your temples. Feel the stretch and release of tension in your upper back and back of your shoulders as you attempt to touch your elbows together. Exhale slowly as you hold for 5 seconds. Return to the starting position, pushing your elbows back and squeezing your shoulder blades together. Repeat for five repetitions.

Finish

Doorway Stretch -
Target Area: Chest and shoulders.

Stand facing a doorway with your arms held up at right angles to your upper body. Slowly lean into a doorway until a comfortable stretch is felt in the

shoulders, chest, and upper back areas. Hold for 15-30 seconds. Repeat twice.

Neck Extension Stretch - Target Area: Neck extensors.

Tilt your neck backwards to a comfortable position. Apply light pressure on your forehead until you feel a comfortable stretch in the front of your neck. Exhale slowly. Hold for 15-30 seconds. Repeat twice.

Side Neck Stretch - Target Area: Side neck muscles.

This stretch is performed by simply tilting your head directly to one side until a comfortable stretch along the sides of the neck. Remember to keep your shoulders as level as possible. Exhale slowly. Hold for 15-30 seconds. Perform twice to each side.

Neck Rotation Stretch - Target Area: Neck rotator muscles.

Keeping your shoulders facing forward, turn your head to one side (as if you are looking over your shoulder). Place your fingers against your chin and gently apply pressure until you feel a comfortable stretch in the neck rotator muscles along the side of the neck. Hold 15-30 seconds. Repeat to the other side. Repeat twice to each side.

ARMS

Forearm Flexor Stretch -
Target Area: Forearm flexor muscles.

Standing or seated in an upright position, extend your arm straight out in front of you at shoulder level. Using your other hand, gently pull the fingers of the extended hand upwards and backwards until a comfortable stretch is felt in the forearm. Hold for 15-30 seconds. Repeat with the other arm. Repeat twice with each arm.

Forearm Extensor Stretch -
Target Area:
Forearm extensor muscles.

Standing or seated in an upright position, extend your arm straight out in front of you at shoulder level. Using your other hand, gently pull the fingers of the extended hand downwards and backwards until a comfortable stretch is felt in the top of the forearm. Hold for 15-30 seconds. Repeat with the other arm. Repeat twice with each arm.

Triceps Stretch -
Target Area: Back of arms and shoulders.

Standing or seated in an upright position, raise your right arm over your head and bend the elbow until your right hand travels behind your head. Grasp the right elbow with your left hand and carefully bring your elbow up and toward the back of your head until a gentle stretch is felt in the back of the right arm near the right shoulder. Exhale slowly. Hold for 15-30 seconds. Repeat with the left arm. Repeat twice with each arm.

Biceps Stretch -
Target Area: Biceps and forearms.

In a standing or seated position, extend your right arm directly out to the side at shoulder height with the palm facing down. Apply light pressure against a wall or fixed object until you feel a comfortable stretch in the biceps region. Hold for 15-30 seconds. Repeat with the left arm. Repeat twice with each arm.

**Triceps/Rotator Cuff Stretch
with Flexi-grip Ball™**
Target Area: Triceps, shoulders, rotator
cuff muscles.

This exercise is performed with the
Flexi-grip Ball™, a useful exercise tool
that can help develop flexibility and
strength in golf-specific muscles. With
your right hand, grasp one handle of
the ball and place the ball behind your
head and shoulders. With your left hand, reach behind your
back and upward to grab the other handle of the ball (as
shown). Gently pull downward with your left hand, while
gently pulling upward with your right hand until a
comfortable stretch is felt in the triceps and shoulder areas.
Hold for 15-30 seconds. Repeat with the other arm. Repeat
twice more with each arm.

As you consistently perform these flexibility exercises,
they will become much easier to do and will be a comfortable
and welcome addition in your daily schedule. You'll notice a
positive change in your body both on and off the golf course!

CHAPTER Five

Strength Training
Playing A Stronger Game of Golf!

"Know your strengths and take advantage of them."

-Greg Norman

For many years, the thought of strength training as preparation for playing great golf was looked upon with considerable skepticism. The thought of stiff, inflexible muscles clouded the minds of many would-be strength trainers. Fortunately, times have changed and many golfers — professionals, amateurs, and "weekend warriors" alike — are now reaping the benefits of increased muscular strength and improved endurance for better golfing performance.

This chapter will provide you with a basic program of strength training exercises that can add power to your swing, improve your range of motion and flexibility, enhance muscular endurance, and increase your control and consistency. In addition, becoming stronger can help you to prevent injury.

It is important to incorporate these basic strengthening exercises with the stretching exercises in Chapter 4. This will help you develop **flexible** muscles and tissues and improve the range of motion in your swing, avoiding the tendency to build stiff, inflexible muscles that can negatively affect the development of good swing habits.

Talk with your qualified golf teaching professional about your particular fitness goals and how to incorporate strength training into your golf preparation routine. Using the exercises from this and the previous chapter, he or she can better guide you in developing specific swing habits and a routine that meets your particular needs and goals.

Major Muscles Used in the Golf Swing

An effective strength training program should target the muscles that are most involved in a typical golf swing (these muscles are illustrated below):

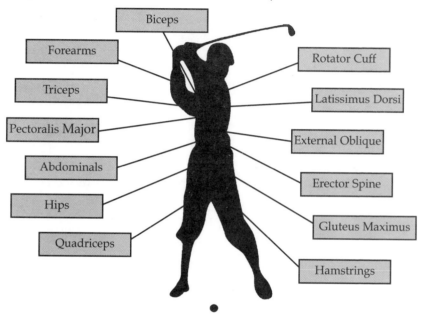

Listed below is the sequence of muscular activity during a golf swing:

1. During the takeaway, the **shoulders** and **arms** initiate movement and are predominantly used. As your weight is transferred back, the muscles of the **outer hip** (hip abductors) come into play. This is followed by the action of the **external obliques** and **abdominals,** which rotate the right hip (left hip if left-handed) to the right and back.
2. The **rotator cuff** muscles (near the shoulders and shoulder

joint) then rotate the arms upward and backward, assisted by the **triceps** and **biceps** (this action is reversed during the downswing).

3. The hips begin the movement down into the ball, while the legs **(quadriceps, hamstrings, gluteus maximus)** provide approximately 80 percent of the power in the golf swing.

4. The midsection **(abdominals, obliques** and **erector spinae**) transfers force from the lower body to the upper body and is responsible for swing acceleration.

5. The upper body **(pectoralis major, latissimus dorsi** and **rotator cuff)** produces the actual swinging motion and plays a major role in generating clubhead speed.

6. Finally, the arms **(biceps, triceps, forearm flexors/extensors)** control the accuracy of the clubhead at impact with the ball, with the **forearm** muscles controlling grip pressure on the club.

Strength Training Benefits

1. Regular strength training increases muscle strength and endurance, allowing you to generate maximum power in your swing and increase clubhead speed upon impact with the ball.

2. Well-trained muscles can improve your control and consistency in your stroke.

3. Strong muscles enhance your overall appearance and increase your confidence - a mental boost for any golfer.

4. Well-balanced and trained muscles reduce your risk for overuse injuries.

5. Strong muscles increase your metabolism for enhanced calorie burning - even when you sleep!

Strength Training Guidelines

⇨ **Warm-up your muscles for 3-5 minutes** - consisting of a low intensity aerobic activity, such as walking or jogging in place, jumping jacks, stationary bicycle, treadmill, or stair climber. This will provide the muscles, tissues, and joints with adequate blood flow and increase working muscle temperature.

⇨ Perform the exercises in the order they appear in this chapter (working your larger muscles first).

⇨ **Stretch <u>before</u>, <u>during</u>, and <u>after</u> each strength training session.** Following the warm-up, you should stretch for 5-10 minutes before performing the strengthening exercises. During the workout, **stretch before and after each exercise.** After the workout, stretch as part of your cool-down for 5-10 minutes. In order for strength training to produce a powerful, yet flexible golf swing, it must be accompanied by regular stretching (stiff, inflexible muscles are a detriment to an efficient swing). <u>**The entire body should be stretched,**</u> utilizing the stretches from Chapter 4. Remember to hold each stretch for a minimum of 15-30 seconds.

⇨ Perform <u>**one set**</u> of each exercise for the recommended number of repetitions. If using a weight in any particular exercise, choose one that allows you to feel the movement comfortably throughout the set and becomes challenging for the last 2 or 3 repetitions.

⇨ **Take 30 seconds to rest and stretch between each exercise.**

⇨ **Strength training** should be performed on three non-consecutive days every week (for example, Monday, Wednesday, and Friday). Allow at least 48 hours between strength workouts. This gives your muscles time to recover before your next session.

⇨ **As you gradually become stronger** (within 2-4 weeks of

<u>consistent</u> strength training), **add one more set** every 2-4 weeks until you have reached three total sets of each exercise. Then increase the weight approximately 10 percent every 2-4 weeks, if desired, to gradually improve strength levels. Remember, don't be in a hurry to gain strength. It is important to get stronger gradually. This helps avoid the development of bulky or stiff muscles that can have a negative impact on your swing.

⇨ **If you are a beginning exerciser,** start by performing only the amount of repetitions that are comfortable for you. Over time, as you become accustomed to regular exercise, you will notice an gradual increase in the ability to perform a greater number of repetitions.

⇨ **Focus on your breathing** and think about the muscles you are working during the exercise. This will help you to relax and increase the effectiveness of the movement. Think about your golfing goals and confidently picture yourself achieving them!

⇨ The strengthening exercises in this chapter can be performed by men and women of all ages, however, consult with your physician and/or physical therapist prior to beginning a strength training program to determine your limitations and/or specific fitness goals.

For convenience, most of the exercises in this chapter can be done in the comfort of your home. All you will need is a pair of light dumbbells, a mat or padded surface, and about 6-10 square feet of space. However, if you would like to work out at a gym or health club and you want to use weight machines for strengthening your muscles, I have provided a **gym routine** at the end of this chapter. This routine utilizes weight resistance machines that are commonly found in most gyms and health clubs.

If you work out at a gym or health club, I suggest you seek the guidance of a certified athletic trainer who is familiar with golf specific training and who can supervise you in a golf-specific weight resistance routine.

Start

Lunge -
Target Area: Thighs, hips, hamstrings, buttocks.

Stand with your feet shoulder width apart, toes pointed straight ahead, hands on your hips. With your left leg, step forward approximately 3-4 feet. Keeping your left knee directly over the left foot and ankle, inhale as you bend your left knee until the left thigh is nearly parallel with the floor. Hold this position for a count of two. Using left thigh strength, exhale and return to the starting position. Perform 10-15 repetitions with each leg.

Finish

(Note: If you experience pain or discomfort in the knees while doing the lunge, stop immediately and consult your physician). As you become stronger with this exercise, you may proceed to holding light dumbbells in your hands (3-10 lb.).

Finish

Squat -
Target Area: Thighs, hips, buttocks, hamstrings.

The squat is one of the best overall conditioning exercises that you can do. Stand with your legs shoulder width apart, knees slightly bent, and toes pointed slightly outward. Keep your body weight centered over the middle of your feet and your arms held straight out in front of you at shoulder height.

Inhale as you drop your buttocks down and back until your thighs are at a point just above parallel with the floor. Hold for a count of two, then exhale as you return to standing position, using front thigh strength to stand up. Do not lock your knees in the standing position (keep them slightly bent). Perform 15-20 repetitions. As you become stronger, you may progress to holding a pair of dumbbells in your hands, using the same technique as the regular squat described above.

Start

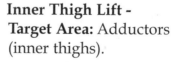

Finish

Inner Thigh Lift -
Target Area: Adductors (inner thighs).

Lie on your side on a mat or padded surface. Place a bench or chair at the level of your feet, placing one foot on the surface

65

of the seat, above the level of the other foot. Holding your legs straight, use inner thigh strength to raise the lower leg up to the level of the top leg. Hold for three seconds, then return to the starting position. Repeat 15-20 times. Turn over and repeat 15-20 times with the other leg. As your inner thigh strength improves, you may wear ankle weights for added resistance.

Outer Thigh Lift -
Target Area: Abductors (outer thighs).

Stand at arms length facing a wall. Place your hands against the wall for balance only (do not lean against the wall). Start with your feet together. Exhale as you raise your right leg outward and upward directly to the side, up to a comfortable height. Hold for one second and inhale as you slowly return to the start. Repeat 15 times with each leg. As your outer thigh strength improves, you may wear ankle weights for added resistance.

Start

Standing Calf Raise -
Target Area: Calves.

Place the balls of your feet on a step or stand on the floor (if you are on a step, allow your heels to sink downward as far as they can go). Hold on to a fixed object, such as a wall, for support. Exhale as you raise up on the balls of your feet as high as you can go. Hold for three seconds at the peak contracted position, then inhale as you slowly return to the start. Perform up to 20-30 repetitions. Note: The picture shows calf raises performed on a calf raise machine, but you can perform the same movement on a step. For added resistance as your strength improves, you may use the calf raise machine (if one is available to you), or you may raise up on one leg at a time during the movement.

Finish

Push-ups
Target Area: Chest, shoulders, triceps.

For men, use the standard push-up position with only the hands and toes in contact with the floor (as pictured below).

Start   **Finish**

For women, place the knees on the ground in a modified push-up position (as pictured below).

Start   **Finish**

Lie face down on a mat or padded surface and place your hands in a push-up position near your shoulders with the fingers pointing forward. Keeping your back straight, exhale as you push your upper body off the floor until your arms are fully extended. Inhale as you slowly return to the starting position, making sure your chest does not come in contact with the floor (it should remain about one inch off the floor at the bottom of the movement). Hold for one second in this bottom position. Perform up to 20-30 repetitions without stopping. Keep your elbows pointed directly out to the sides throughout the exercise.

Start

Side Lateral Raises -
Target Area: Shoulders.

Standing or seated in an upright position with your feet shoulder width apart, grasp a pair of dumbbells and hold them against your thighs at your sides as shown (use 3-5 lb. dumbbells when first beginning this exercise). Bend your arms slightly and bend slightly forward at the waist, maintaining this position throughout the exercise.

Keeping your palms down toward the floor, exhale as you use shoulder strength to raise the dumbbells upward and directly out to the sides in an arc-shaped motion until the weights reach shoulder level. At this top position,

Finish

rotate your slightly (as if pouring a glass of water with each hand). Hold for three seconds and inhale as you slowly lower your arms to the starting position. Repeat for 10-15 repetitions. Note: If you are not yet strong enough to use weights in this exercise, you may simply move your arms during the movement for 20-30 repetitions until you gradually become strong enough to use light dumbbells.

Internal Shoulder Rotation
Target Area: Rotator cuff.

Start

Lie on your left side on a floor or bench with a rolled up towel or pillow placed under your head for support. Start with a 3-8 lb. dumbbell for this exercise (for maximum safety, never exceed 10-15 lb. in this exercise). Keep your left arm bent at 90 degrees with the left elbow tucked in at your side. Starting from a parallel position with the floor, rotate the left hand upward, toward the chest. Slowly return to the starting position. Repeat 10-15 times. Repeat on your right side for 10-15 times.

Finish

External Shoulder Rotation -
Target Area: Rotator cuff.

Lie on your left side on a floor or bench with your left arm bent at 90 degrees under your head for support. With a very

Start

light dumbbell in your right hand (for maximum safety, never exceed 8-10 lb. in this exercise) and keeping the right elbow bent at 90 degrees, lift the weight upward, keeping the elbow stationary against your right side (the elbow acts as a hinge), rotate the weight upward to a point as far vertical as possible. Slowly lower the weight to the starting position. Repeat 10-15 times. Lie on your right side and repeat 10-15 times with your left arm.

Finish

Shoulder Shrug -
Target Area: Trapezius (upper back) and forearms.

You may do this exercise standing or seated. Hold a pair of light dumbbells at your sides (use 5-10 lb. dumbbells when

Start

first performing this exercise) with your arms fully extended. Exhale as you lift your shoulders as high up and to the rear as possible. Hold this peak contracted position for two seconds before inhaling as

Finish

70

you slowly return to the start position. Perform 15-20 repetitions.

Start

Finish

Triceps Kickbacks -
Target Area: Triceps muscles (back of the upper arm).

Grasp a light dumbbell in your right hand (use 3-8 lb. dumbbells when first performing this exercise) and place your knees and left arm on a bench (as shown). Hold your right arm at 90 degrees with the palm facing your body and your right elbow held firmly against your side. Begin the movement by exhaling as you push the weight backward and upward (using triceps strength only, do not lift the elbow) until your arm is straight and parallel with the floor. Hold this peak contracted position for two seconds and slowly return to the start. Repeat 15-20 times with each arm.

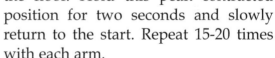

Wrist Curls -
Target Area: Forearm flexor muscles.

Do this exercise seated. With your forearms supported on your thighs (as shown) or on a bench or chair, slowly lift a pair of light dumbbells (use 3-8 lb.

Start

dumbbells when first performing this exercise), palms facing up, by curling the weight upward toward your forearms. Hold and contract the forearm muscles for two seconds at the top of the movement. Slowly lower the dumbbells below the level of your knees or the bench and allow the weight to stretch your forearms fully at this bottom position. Repeat for 15-20 repetitions. You can also do this with one arm at a time for more intensity.

Finish

Reverse Wrist Curl -
Target Area: Forearm extensor muscles.

Do this exercise seated. With your forearms supported on your thighs (as shown) or on a bench or chair, slowly lift a pair of light dumbbells (use 3-5 lb. dumbbells when first performing this exercise), palm down, by lifting the weight upward toward your forearms. Hold and contract the forearms muscles for two seconds at the top of the movement. Slowly lower the dumbbells below the level of your knees or the bench and allow the weight to stretch your forearms fully at this bottom

Midpoint

position. Repeat for 15-20 repetitions. You can also do this with one arm at a time for more intensity.

| Start | Midpoint | Finish |

Wrist Rotation -
Target Area: Wrists and forearms.

Using the same starting position as the above two exercises, grasp **one** light dumbbell in one hand (for maximum effectiveness, never exceed 8-10 lb. in either hand) with your palm facing up. Slowly rotate the dumbbell to a palms-down position, holding for a second, then return slowly to a palms-up position. Repeat 15-20 times. Repeat with the other hand. Note: You can also perform this exercise with a golf club before you tee off!

Lying Hyperextension -
Target Area:
Lower Back/erector spinae.

Lie on your stomach on the floor on a mat or padded surface. Keep your arms at your sides with your palms up. Begin by lifting your upper body, raising your head, shoulders and chest as a single unit until they are a comfortable distance above the floor (several inches). Pause five seconds, then lower the upper body back down to the starting position. Exhale on the lift and inhale as you lower your body

73

back down. As your conditioning improves, put your hands out in front of you when you lift (as pictured above). From there, you can progress to raising your opposite arm and leg together, or both arms and legs at the same time for an even greater challenge. Repeat 15-20 times.

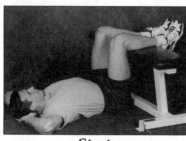

Start

Finish

**Abdominal Crunches -
Target Area:** Abdominals.

Lie on the floor on your back with your legs resting on a bench or at 45 degrees. Place your hands behind your head and keep your elbows pointed outwards.

Using abdominal strength, curl your shoulders and upper back up off the floor, exhaling as you go up. Try to keep your lower back firmly pressed into the floor. Hold for two seconds at this peak-contracted position, then inhale as you slowly lower your upper back to the floor. Begin by doing 15-20 repetitions, working up to 25-50 repetitions without stopping.

As you become stronger with this exercise, you may progress to crossing your arms and holding a 5-10 lb. weight on your chest.

Finish

**Twisting Crunches -
Target Area:** Side abdominals.

Using the same starting position as the above exercise, exhale as you lift your right elbow and shoulder toward the left knee. Hold for two seconds. Inhale as you return to the starting position and repeat with the other arm and shoulder. Perform 15 repetitions to each side, working up to 25-50 repetitions without stopping.

Finish

**Knee Tuck Crunches -
Target Area:** Lower Abs.

Using the same starting position as the above two exercises, bring your knees into your chest area using lower abdominal strength. Keep your knees in this position throughout the exercise. Using abdominal strength, exhale as you curl your shoulders and upper back off the floor toward your knees until you feel a peak contraction in the lower abdominal muscles. Hold this position for two seconds. Inhale as you slowly lower your upper back to the floor. Repeat for 15 repetitions, working up to 25-50 without stopping.

Gym Routine

The following routine can be performed for increasing muscular strength by using equipment commonly found in a gym or health club.

Workout Guidelines

⇨ Warm up for 5- 10 minutes, using a treadmill, stationary bike, stair climber, etc., then stretch the entire body for 5-10 minutes. After your gym workout, cool-down and stretch for 5-10 minutes.

⇨ Take 30 seconds to rest and stretch between each exercise.

⇨ Perform one set of each exercise for the first 4-6 weeks, then add a set every 4-6 weeks until you reach three total sets of each exercise.

⇨ Workout on three non-consecutive days each week (for example, Monday, Wednesday, Friday), allowing 48 hours between strength workouts.

⇨ The workout takes between 30-60 minutes to perform. Perform each exercise, in the order they are listed, for maximum safety and benefit.

#1. Leg Extension - In a seated position, grasp the handles at your sides and use quadriceps (front thigh) strength to lift your feet upward to a straight-leg position. Hold for two seconds, squeezing the thighs, and slowly lower the weight. Repeat 15-20 times.

#2. Squat - As previously described in this chapter. As you progress in lower body strength, you may use a barbell placed on your shoulders and upper back for added resistance. Perform 12-15 repetitions.

#3. Leg Curl - Lie face down on the machine's surface and place your knees at the edge of the surface closest to the padded machine arm. Hook your heels under the roller and begin by pulling the weight toward your buttocks, keeping your hips down to prevent lower back strain. Use hamstring strength to curl the weight up until the legs are as fully bent as possible. Hold for two seconds and slowly return to a straight leg position. Repeat 15-20 times.

#4. <u>Calf Raise</u> - As previously described in this chapter. As you progress in calf strength, you may use the calf raise machine with added weight for resistance. Perform up to 20-30 repetitions before increasing the weight gradually.

#5. <u>Bench Press</u> - Lie down on a bench with a barbell above your head (you may also use dumbbells held in each hand). Grasp the barbell a little wider than shoulder width. Keeping the weight centered over your chest, slowly lower the bar while keeping the elbows directly out to the sides. As the bar lightly touches your chest, push the weight back to the starting position. Repeat 12-15 times.

#6. <u>Seated Rows</u> - Grasp the handle of a low-pulley rowing machine. Sitting upright, pull the handle into your lower rib cage, keeping your elbows in, close to your sides. Expand your chest while squeezing the back muscles together, slightly arching your back. Hold for two seconds and slowly return to the start. Avoid rounding the back here. Perform 12-15 repetitions.

#7. <u>External/Internal Shoulder Rotation</u> - As previously described in this chapter. This exercise also provides a chance to rest between more intense movements. Perform 10-15 repetitions with each arm.

#8. <u>Wrist Curls</u> - As previously described in this chapter. As you improve your strength in the forearm muscles, you may use a barbell with weight added for increased resistance. Perform 15-20 repetitions with each arm.

#9. <u>Wrist Rotation</u> - As previously described in this chapter. Perform 15-20 repetitions with each arm.

#10. <u>Hyperextension (Lower Back Exercise)</u> - Use extreme care when using this machine if you have a weak lower back. Tuck your heels under the rear pad of the machine and cross your arms over your chest. Keeping your legs slightly bent to take pressure off the lower back, allow the upper body to hang down directly from the hips. Using back and buttock strength, raise your chest to a position parallel with the floor, and no higher. Pause for one second and slowly return to the start. Work up to 12-15 repetitions. When you become stronger in the lower back, you may hold light weight 5-15 lb. against your chest during this exercise.

#11. <u>Abdominal Crunches</u> - As previously described in this chapter. As you become stronger in your stomach muscles, you may progress to adding a weighted plate on your chest during the crunch movement. Perform 15-20 repetitions, working your way up to 25-50 repetitions over time.

"It's not just enough to swing at the ball. You've got to loosen your girdle and really let the ball have it."
- Babe Didrikson Zaharias

CHAPTER Six

Cardiovascular Fitness
The Key to More Energy —
From the First Tee
through the 18th Hole!

"The harder you work, the luckier you get."
-Gary Player

Consider this scenario:

1st *through the* 11th *hole* - You have energy! **Result: you're playing well and consistently for your first 11 holes.**

12th *hole* - You start to feel a drop in your energy. As you follow through on your drive, your grip loosens. **S-L-I-C-E!** The ball sails off the fairway to the right. **Result: bogey.**

15th *hole* - From the fairway, you attempt a 3-iron shot to the green. However, your fatigue has affected your ability to fully concentrate on this shot. As a result, you are momentarily distracted as you initiate your swing. This throws off your concentration and you send the ball over the green and into the woods. **Result: double-bogey.**

18th *hole* - You are feeling fatigued. Your concentration is fading, and your effectiveness has gradually deteriorated over the last few holes. You've lost your focus. You start thinking about your inconsistent play instead of the upcoming shot. In fact, you just want to get this round over with. Naturally, you hurry through your last few shots. **Result: double-bogey, and a good round gone bad.**

This preceding scenario is all-too-common among many golfers. Oftentimes, a golfer will suffer a drop in energy as a round progresses. Not surprisingly, this has adverse effects, both physical and mental. It results in the loss of ability to maintain a consistent stroke. The mind tends to wander and that all important element of intensity disappears as fatigue sets in.

What can be done to fight this late-round fatigue?
How can that drop in energy be prevented?
Answer: By taking the time to become aerobically fit!

Cardiovascular (aerobic) exercise improves your endurance, control, mental focus, and confidence - helping you play your best golf — from the first tee right through to the final hole! In addition, among the other benefits that cardiovascular fitness brings include:

1. An increased ability to fight off fatigue
2. An improved ability to remain focused
3. A reduced chance of injury
4. A greater ability to maintain a higher level of energy for a longer period of time.

In golf, your ability to remain consistent and effective depends largely upon your ability to completely focus on each individual shot. As world-renowned instructor David Leadbetter advises, "being tired coming down the last few holes can lead to letting a few shots slip away mentally." To prevent this from happening and finish a round strong, you must be able to maintain a high level of energy for the entire round. Being aerobically fit will give you the extra energy you need to maintain your competitive edge!

Cardiovascular Training Guidelines

Before deciding on which exercise is right for you, it's important to consider the following criteria:

1) Your present level of aerobic fitness (beginners should start at a low level of intensity, gradually increasing effort over time).

2) Existing health problems (for example, those with high blood pressure, a history of heart disease, musculoskeletal injury, etc. should obtain a physician's approval before beginning any aerobic exercise).

3) Your age (as we age, we gradually lose flexibility, strength, and endurance).

4) Aerobic fitness goals (including: building more energy on the golf course, increasing control in your swing, improving mental focus and confidence, burning fat and losing weight).

5) Time constraints (certain exercise activity is more appropriate for those with limited time for exercise. Activities such as tennis, racquetball, and aerobic dance, for instance, take longer to perform).

Cardiovascular training is composed of the following elements: 1) a warm-up, 2) proper exercise intensity, 3) appropriate exercise frequency and duration, 4) a cool-down period.

1) A brief warm-up period of approximately 5-10 minutes. This will include 3-5 minutes of low intensity aerobic exercise (similar to the exercise being performed), followed by 3-5 minutes of stretching the primary muscles used in the exercise (for example, stretching the legs before riding a stationary bicycle). Among the major reasons for a warm-up are the following:

a. Increased blood flow to working muscles
b. Improved flexibility in those muscles
c. Reduced chance for injury

   d. Increased oxygen consumption (providing more energy)
   e. Prevention of muscle soreness
   f. Improved muscular feedback
   g. Improved coordination
   h. Enhanced mental focus and concentration

2) Intensity of exercise - In order to achieve the many benefits of cardiovascular exercise, the intensity of exercise should remain in your "target zone" for a minimum of 20 minutes (again, if you are a beginning exerciser, you may start with lower times, such as 5-15 minutes, working your way up to 20 minutes over time).

If you are a beginning exerciser over 60 years of age, begin an aerobic exercise program by walking in your neighborhood for 5-10 minutes, 3 days each week, working your way up to 20-30 minutes by the end of the first 8 weeks)

This "target zone" is reflected by your heart rate (beats per minute) during exercise and is equivalent to 60-80% of your maximum heart rate (start at 50-60% if you are unconditioned, up to 80% if you are at a high level of aerobic fitness).

To obtain your target heart rate, take 220 and subtract your age (this number represents your **maximum heart rate**). Then multiply by .6 if you are a beginning exerciser up to .8 if you are in great shape.

For example, Nancy is 35 years old and is a *beginning* exerciser, so she would shoot for 60 percent of her maximum heart rate as follows:

Target heart rate =
220 - 35 (Nancy's age) = 185 (maximum heart rate) x .6 (60 percent)
= 111 beats per minute

To figure your heart rate, take your pulse at the carotid artery of the neck. Using the tips of your index and middle fingers (don't use the thumb, it has it's own pulse), gently place the fingertips over the carotid artery (just to the side of the Adam's Apple) and apply light pressure.

Count the heart beat for **ten seconds** (be careful not to apply too much pressure to avoid the possibility of dizziness or fainting). Take that number and multiply by 6 to obtain heart beats per minute. *Take your pulse every 3 minutes during the exercise to make sure you are in the target zone.*

The "Talk Test"

An easier way to make sure you are exercising at the proper intensity is referred to as the "talk test." This method for reaching your target zone is performed by exercising up to a point where you can comfortably carry on a conversation with someone, without becoming out of breath. If you cannot comfortably carry on a conversation without becoming out of breath, reduce the intensity of the exercise. This "talk test" is especially beneficial for those who are just beginning a cardiovascular exercise program (or who are over 60 years of age) because this method helps you start out at a lower level of exercise intensity.

3) Proper exercise <u>frequency</u> and <u>duration</u> of training - You should perform **a minimum of 3-5 aerobic exercise sessions per week.** The specific duration of aerobic exercise depends on your present level of aerobic fitness. For example, if you are presently:

Unconditioned - Perform 5-10 minutes of continuous aerobic exercise for 1-2 times each day, 3 days per week. Allow a day off in between exercise sessions in order to achieve best results and to recover from your previous exercise session(s). Gradually increase your time in minutes during the first 4-6 weeks of aerobic training. After a 4-6 week period of regular exercise, you may progress to the next stage.

A recent beginner to exercise - Perform 10-20 minutes of continuous aerobic exercise, 3-5 days per week. Remain in this stage for 4-10 weeks before progressing to the next stage.

At an average level of aerobic fitness - Perform 15-45 minutes of continuous aerobic exercise, 3-5 days per week. Remain in at this level for 4-10 weeks before progressing to the next level.

At a high level of aerobic fitness - Perform 30-60 minutes of continuous aerobic exercise, 3-5 days per week to maintain this level.

4) <u>**A brief cool-down period**</u> - of approximately 3-10 minutes, depending on the duration of the exercise performed (longer exercise requires an extended cool-down period). This will include 3-8 minutes of low intensity aerobic exercise, followed by 2-3 minutes of stretching the primary muscles used in the exercise. Among the major reasons for a cool-down are the following:

a. gradually decrease your heart rate
b. ensure adequate circulation of blood to the heart, brain, and muscles
c. decrease muscle spasm and cramping
d. reduce the risk of lightheadedness or fainting

Remember to conclude the cool-down period with a couple minutes of easy stretching of the muscles predominantly used during the aerobic exercise. For example, jumping rope would be followed by stretching the legs and upper body.

In addition to the many valuable benefits that can be seen on the golf course, aerobic exercise will help you to:

- Burn body fat / decrease body fat stores / lose unwanted weight
- Strengthen your heart and reduce the risk of cardiovascular (heart) disease
- Build your muscle (increased muscle tone leads to an improved ability to burn calories and fat)
- Improve blood circulation and delivery of nutrients throughout your body
- Lower your blood pressure and resting heart rate
- Improve your sleep patterns
- Decrease total cholesterol levels/increase good cholesterol (HDL's)
- Decrease anxiety and depression

Popular cardiovascular (aerobic) exercises include the following:

walking	cycling	swimming	rowing
soccer	jogging	stair climbing	tennis
basketball	racquetball	aerobic dance	step aerobics
handball	jump rope	backpacking	hiking

Choose two or three of your favorite aerobic exercises and do them each week. This will add variety to your golf fitness training and help keep you motivated!

Other cardiovascular training tips:

- **Use your goals chart** to set your cardiovascular (aerobic)goals, and remember to record your aerobic exercise sessions in your training journal. Be specific, just as you would with your weight training or golf performance goals (for example, increasing overall energy on the golf course, improving confidence and relaxation, losing body fat, lowering blood pressure, reduce cholesterol levels, etc.).
- Incorporating your flexibility and strength training exercises into your regular schedule will also enhance your aerobic workouts greatly. All of your exercises combined will give you more overall energy on and off the golf course.
- While on the golf course, try to walk in between your shots as much as possible. This will improve your level of aerobic fitness and help you to prepare for your next shot by keeping your muscles and joints warm and loose.

Aerobic exercise cautions:

- Stop exercise immediately if you experience chest pain, lightheadedness, or dizziness
- Avoid exercising for at least 90 minutes following a meal
- Do not perform intense exercise in hot or humid environments, or at altitudes above 5,000 feet
- Do not exercise during periods of illness, such as colds or flu
- Avoid exercise if you have an injury that can be potentially aggravated by increased activity
- Avoid exercise during times of emotional trauma (such as death, divorce, loss of job, etc.)

- Do not exercise after consuming alcohol, stimulating beverages (coffee, tea, etc.), or if taking certain medications

Many golfers underestimate the demands placed upon them during the average round of golf. A golfer can play **4-5 hours** and cover as many as **3-4 miles** during an 18-hole round of golf. Even when you ride in a golf cart, you spend a great deal of time walking and on your feet. If you aren't aerobically fit, you simply won't be able to maintain that level of energy as well as you could if you participate in regular aerobic exercise.

Remember, as your overall level of cardiovascular fitness improves, your energy and endurance on the golf course will improve dramatically. This will result in better scores and a greater enjoyment of the game!

CHAPTER Seven

Golfing Nutrition
Your Secret Advantage

> **"Golfers find it a very trying matter to turn at the waist, more particularly if they have a lot of waist to turn."**
> -Harry Vardon

An often overlooked element in the battle for energy and stamina on the golf course is **good nutrition.** A round of golf can be physically and mentally draining. It requires continuous energy to be consistent throughout the round, especially after the first nine holes. This is when your energy and endurance are put to the ultimate test, and the importance of sound nutritional principles takes center stage!

As a golfer, **YOU** are in control of what you do to prepare yourself before you play. If your goal is to play at your best, you need to eat the types of foods that are going to enhance performance, not diminish it. Eating a nutritious, balanced diet, consisting of a variety of foods, can give you that competitive edge. You'll notice a dramatic and positive effect on your golfing performance, right from the first tee. That's what I mean when I say that the unseen and often overlooked element of good nutrition is your secret advantage. Never underestimate its impact!

Many times a golfer can prepare themselves with hours of practice on the range, the putting green, or in the bunkers. But, when it comes right down to playing at the next level — beating your playing partners, playing your best round, or winning that tournament — it's what you eat that can often make the difference between success or failure. It's this unseen advantage that sets you apart from the rest, powerfully impacting both your physical abilities, as well as your mental performance. Remember, when it comes down to **what** you eat and drink - **you** are in control - whether you're on the golf course, at home, or dining out.

Believe it or not, you can burn up a lot of calories playing golf (2,000 to as much as 3,500 a day if you are an active golfer). These calories need to be consumed properly before and during your play, following a few simple rules of good nutrition. These basic rules can make the difference between playing an average round and an exceptional one!

"Rules" of Good Nutrition

First and foremost, eating a balanced diet, composed of a variety of nutritious foods, will lead to improved energy and health. Try to stick to foods that are low in fat, low in sugar, and high in fiber, and remember the following suggested "rules":

Rule #1:
EAT LESS FAT!

Fat calories (such as ice cream, fried foods, candy bars, etc.) can contribute to unwanted body fat, slow down your metabolism, and leave you feeling sluggish and unenergized. In the quest for peak performance on the golf course, this can spell disaster. Fats also tend to be digested slowly, leaving less room in your stomach for valuable **complex carbohydrates.** Carbohydrates are stored in the liver and muscles, and are used for **long-term, sustained energy.**

Rule #2:

DON'T SKIP MEALS!

This can result in a decreased metabolism and loss of energy. When you skip a meal, your body goes into the "store fat mode" and begins to slow down. For optimum energy, I recommend getting into the habit of eating small meals every 3-4 hours per day. If you believe that eating every 3-4 hours requires too much of your time, then eat a <u>minimum</u> of 3 nutritious meals a day. These meals should be composed of 60-65% carbohydrates, 15-20% protein, and 15-30% fat calories.

For best results, follow the 'thirds rule' when you eat - two-thirds of your plate should be carbohydrates (for example; vegetables, starches, and fruits), and one-third should be protein (for example - poultry, fish, lean beef, low-fat cheese). Remember, it's better to eat a large-sized meal for breakfast every morning as opposed to later in the evening. This helps to increase energy and stabilize your appetite throughout the entire day.

Rule #3:

READ FOOD LABELS!

It's a great idea to get in the habit of reading food labels and to become aware of the distribution of calories (such as: carbohydrates, fat, protein, sugar, fiber) in each meal. If you do this, you will begin to automatically know what foods are good for you and what foods to stay away from. Try to stick with foods that are **high in complex carbohydrates and fiber** and **low in fat and sugar.** To determine what percentage of a meal is composed of fat, for example, divide the *calories from fat* by the *total calories per serving.*

91

Example:
Bowl of Oatmeal (Apple & Cinnamon flavor)

Calories per serving................**170**
Calories from fat.....................**15**
Percent of total calories from fat equals

.88 (approximately **9 percent**)

Definitely under the recommended 15-30% calories from fat!
(A good choice!)

<u>*WEIGHT LOSS*</u>*: If your goal is fat/weight loss, you should aim to lose no more than 1-2 lb. per week. Eating sensibly and exercising will help you lose the weight in an efficient and gradual manner. Chances are good that the fat/weight will stay off if it's lost gradually, as opposed to losing it "overnight". Losing weight too quickly results in a loss of precious water and muscle, and can lead to serious health risks. It's important to remember that muscles provide your body with the ability to burn fat, and losing muscle decreases your ability to burn that fat.*

Rule #4:

START A FOOD DIARY

To maximize efficiency in fat/weight loss and nutrition, as well as to improve your performance on the golf course, you must become aware of the foods you normally eat. Recording your meals in a **food diary** provides many benefits (*see sample food diary in Appendix B*). Keeping track of the foods you eat will help you to:

1) *plan and prepare your meals more efficiently,*
2) *eat a balanced and nutritious diet,*
3) *stay motivated to stick to your eating plan,*
4) *maintain higher energy levels for improved golfing performance.*

This really works! Use your food diary to record your thoughts and feelings during each meal, at the end of each day, and the end of each week. This will give you an insight into what and why you are eating certain kinds of foods.

In addition, at the end of each week, record your performance levels, such as: golfing performance, adherence to eating goals (such as eating low fat, low sugar, high carbohydrate, high fiber meals), and your mental state (attitude, motivation, feelings about your golfing performance, etc.). Be patient and consistent in your record keeping. In just a little time, you will begin to feel more in control and you'll notice a difference in both your attitude and golfing ability. Don't be surprised if your golfing partners want to know your secret!

Rule #5:
DRINK PLENTY OF WATER!

Adequate water intake is extremely important for all golfers. **Do not wait until you're thirsty to drink water**, since you can become partially dehydrated before your body signals that you are thirsty. Golfers are often at risk for dehydration, especially in the hot summer months when perspiration increases. When water loss through sweat is greater than 2 percent, performance can be affected. At 3 percent water loss, the golfer may even experience heat cramps or fatigue. Follow these suggestions for optimal

performance:
1) Drink about eight 8-oz. glasses of water the day before you play.
2) About two hours before play, drink 16-20 oz.
3) 15-30 minutes before play, drink 6-16 oz.
4) During the round, drink 3-7 oz. of water every 15-20 minutes.
5) Drink it <u>chilled</u> for better absorption.

Do your best to limit your *caffeine* and *alcohol* intake, as these drugs actually rob your body of precious water and can also lead to dehydration, fatigue, or heat cramps.

Pre-Round and On-the-Course Nutrition

The day before you play your round of golf, you should consume mostly complex carbohydrate foods such as whole-grain cereals and breads, pasta, rice, potatoes, or beans. This will better prepare your body and dramatically enhance your energy and endurance levels on the day you play. Simple carbohydrates such as fruits, fruit juices, and other sweet foods are also used for energy, but not quite as efficiently as complex carbohydrates.

Choosing good food while out on the course can often be a difficult task. Try planning your meals and snacks ahead of time and bring your own nutritious snacks to the course (*for "Power Snack" recipes, see Appendix D*). Here are some good foods to eat while out on the course that will help keep your energy level on high!

pretzels	*raw vegetables*	*rice cakes*	*vegetable juice*
bagels	*dry cereal snacks*	*trail mix*	*fat-free cookies*
sports drinks	*popcorn-no butter*	*cooked rice*	*cooked noodles*
fruits	*lowfat muffins*	*dried fruits*	*granola bars*

Some foods to avoid while out on the course are:

hot dogs	*sausages*	*cheeses*	*hamburgers*
soda	*chocolate bars*	*beer*	*coffee*
pizza	*french fries*	*donuts*	*potato chips*
butter	*croissants*	*most candy*	*ice cream*

Eating habits are not always easy to adjust, so make changes gradually. When playing golf, take along some of the suggested healthier foods listed above. Gradually, in a relatively short period of time (usually within 2-4 weeks or so, depending on how often you play) you will achieve increased energy and improved endurance. As a result, you'll be **motivated** to eat better foods. Soon you'll begin to search out foods that will keep your energy level high for an entire round!

"The secret to longevity is keeping your weight down, not smoking, limiting your toddies and getting plenty of rest."

-Tommy Bolt

CHAPTER Eight

"Oh, My Aching Back"
Preventing Golf Injury

"Golf is like many other sports that require the athlete to be in top condition BEFORE they play, not just when they perform poorly or suffer injury."

-Butch Harmon
Instructor to Tiger Woods

You're on the 8th hole. It's a long par 5, and you've just hit your drive 260 yards down the middle of the fairway. You're looking at 240 yards to the center of the green and a chance for an eagle! You decide to pull out the big stick and go for it, holding nothing back. You start your backswing, knowing in the back of your mind that you need to crush the ball to even get it close to the flag. You take your swing, and suddenly you feel something — that familiar pain hits. Your lower back screams out in agony, and you soon realize that you won't be swinging your clubs again for quite some time. "Why did this happen to me?" you wonder.

Has it happened to **you**? It happens to many golfers. Studies show that more than half of all golfers suffer a golf-related injury. I know what you're probably thinking - injuries can happen in more active sports such as football and basketball, where there is a lot of physical contact - but golf? Well, I've got news for you. It can happen on the golf course, too.

Consult your physician immediately if you should have an accident or injury on the golf course (or anywhere else, for that matter). Remember to seek a physician's guidance concerning when it is safe for you to resume play following an accident or injury. In addition, I recommend that you seek instruction from a qualified golf professional who will show you the proper swing mechanics to improve your game and reduce your chances of sustaining a golfing injury.

Considering the fact that the typical golf swing compresses and stretches many of the muscles, tendons, ligaments, and joints in a golfer's body, it's no wonder that injuries occur. These injuries can adversely affect your swing and your ability to concentrate, and can take away your enjoyment of the game. The question is, "What can you do to prevent injuries from happening?"

Prevention is the Cure

The first step in preventing injury is to become aware of the factors that can contribute to injury. Among these factors include the following:

• *Improper warm-up* (Stretch *before, during,* and *after* your round(s). You should spend a minimum of 5-10 minutes stretching your entire body even before you swing your first club).
• *Overuse* (for example, hitting too many balls at the driving range. Repeated stress on muscles, tissues, and joints can result in many common injuries, including "golfer's elbow", rotator cuff and lower back strain).
• *Muscular weakness* (weaker muscles fatigue faster and can lead to faulty swing mechanics. For example, weak abdominal muscles place dangerous stress on the lower back and hips, resulting in a loss of balance, control, and power).
• *Muscular imbalance* (often causes the body to overcompensate for weaker or inflexible muscles by placing

additional stress on the major muscles used in the swing. For example, weak hip rotator muscles can cause the lower back to absorb too much of the swing force, leading to potential low back injury).

• **Lack of flexibility** - the inability to achieve full range of motion at crucial points during the swing (such as the top of the backswing, at impact with the ball, and during the follow-through) contributes to ineffective and potentially dangerous swing habits.

• **Poor swing mechanics** - poor swing mechanics can place the body in unbalanced and potentially dangerous positions during the swing and can, for example, lead to an improper sequence of muscular action, which can lead to injury. Visit your local golf pro who can teach you proper swing mechanics.

• **Stressful living** - muscular tension affects your body's ability to relax and perform at an efficient level. Tension also reduces flexibility and can lead to poor posture.

• **Poor posture** - contributes to the development of ineffective and harmful swing habits.

Common Injury Sites

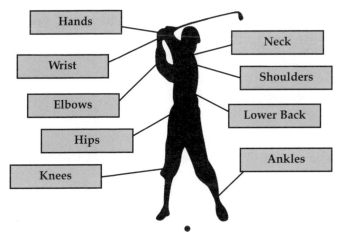

The most commonly injured areas on a golfer are pictured above. In a typical golf swing, a golfer predominantly uses the muscles of the legs, hips, back, abdominals, chest, shoulders, arms, and hands. Developing strength and flexibility in each respective muscle group is essential in preventing golf-related injury.

Preventive Exercises

Oftentimes, it is the golfer with a lower level of fitness who becomes susceptible to a golf-related injury. Regular golf-specific exercise will increase the mobility in joints and tissues, giving you better range of motion and helping you to handle the constant force of a golf swing. Well-conditioned golfers can resist the stresses placed upon their bodies. More specifically, muscles, ligaments, joints, and tendons that are flexible and strong will tend to tolerate the pulling and straining that occurs during a typical golf swing.

To help prevent injury and increase the effectiveness of the exercises that follow in this chapter, perform a warm-up before beginning the exercises (such as stationary bike, walking or jogging in place, etc.), then begin first with the stretches, followed by the strengthening exercises.

Proceed at an easy, slow pace. Start with what you feel comfortable doing (one set of each exercise is okay). Remember, _comfort is the key!_ Gradually work up to the recommended amount of repetitions and sets for each exercise (see previous chapters on exercise techniques for the recommended numbers of repetitions and sets). Also, remember to cool-down after completing the entire series of exercises (see chapter on cardiovascular training for examples of cool-down techniques).

Try to stretch a little every day (at home, at work, and especially at the golf course, as you will see in the next chapter). Make it a routine part of your day. Performing the following stretches (especially those for the lower back) first thing in the morning when you rise is a great way to get yourself going and to improve the flow of blood to your working muscles. This is especially effective if you have stiff or tight muscles in the early morning hours. Warming up weaker areas of your body with a few simple stretches will prepare you for your day and can dramatically reduce the chances of pulling or straining those weaker muscles.

Listed below are some of the most effective injury-preventing exercises and their corresponding benefits (*refer to chapters 4 and 5 for the related exercise descriptions*).

(Note: Focus on your breathing when performing these exercises. Breath in through your nose and exhale slowly through the mouth. This way of breathing aids in relaxing you mind and body and increases the effectiveness of the exercises).

INJURY SITE	EXERCISE	BENEFIT
	Knee Huggers	Increases lower back flexibility
	Wall Sits	Improves posture
Lower Back & Trunk:	**Angry Cat**	Releases tension in back
	Lying Hyperextensions	Strengthens the lower back
	Trunk Rotation	Improves flexibility in trunk
	Trunk Flexion	Same as the above
	Side Bend Stretch	Lowers the risk of injury to rib cage and trunk muscles

	Crunches	Strengthens stomach muscles which help to relieve back strain
	Hamstring Stretches	Release pressure in back by increasing flexibility in back of legs

(Note: The following two exercises help to prevent "Golfer's Elbow" or medial epicondylitis, a common golfing injury that affects the tendons of the forearm muscles. It is commonly caused by repeated ball striking and/or weak forearm flexor muscles).

Elbows:	**Wrist Curls**	Strengthens forearms
	Forearm Stretches	Increases forearm flexibility
Wrists:	**Wrist Rotations**	Strengthens the muscles that surround and protect the wrist
Knees:	**Leg Extensions**	Strengthens the muscles that help to protect the knees
	Leg Curls	Same as the above
	Quadriceps Stretch	Improves flexibility in thighs
	Hamstring Stretch	Improves hamstring flexibility

(Note: Many of these stretches and strengthening exercises will improve your conditioning in other areas of the body as they help to protect the areas they are directly working).

Neck:	**Neck Rotation**	Protects the neck rotator muscles
	Side Neck Tilt	Improves neck flexibility
	Neck Extension	Same as the above
	Neck Flexion	Same as the above
Shoulders:	**Internal Rotation**	Strengthens rotator cuff muscles
	External Rotation	Same as the above
	Side Lateral Raise	Strengthens shoulder muscles
	Shoulder Shrug	Helps protect shoulders and neck
	Rotator Cuff Stretch	Protects rotator cuff muscles
	Doorway Stretch	Improves freedom of movement and range of motion in shoulders
Ankles:	**Calf Raise**	Strengthens muscles that help to protect the ankle and joint
	Calf Stretch	Improves flexibility in calf muscles for better joint mobility

Proper Body Mechanics

Along with the prevention of injury through exercise, common rules of good posture and proper body mechanics apply when you're out there on the course, as well as in your daily life.

The following examples illustrate:

- poor body mechanics that contribute to injury,
- proper body mechanics that can keep you safe and injury-free!

Lining up a putt -

YES

NO

Knees bent, back straight and upper body is held upright. Even if you are unable to fully bend the knees as pictured above, it is important to slightly bend them to take pressure off the lower back.

Knees are locked, back is excessively rounded, neck muscles are strained. This position can lead to lower back, neck, and knee injury over time and also negatively affect your concentration as you are lining up to putt.

Placing your tee in the ground -

YES   **NO**

One or both knees bent, using your club for support, staying close to the tee you are reaching for. This is the same desired position as picking up your ball from the cup (as pictured).

Knees are straight, putting excess pressure on lower back, hand is too far from body when reaching for the tee, neck is straining, not properly using club for support. These positions, over time, can lead to injury in the lower back, shoulders, neck, and knees.

Proper and safe swing form -

YES

Weight is balanced and the back is not excessively arched in the follow-through. The golfer finishes with an upright stance.

NO

During the follow-through, the golfer goes into a "Reverse-C" position, putting excessive pressure on the lower back.

Seated position in your golf cart -

YES

Sitting upright, chin up, feet flat on floor of cart, knees bent, arm(s) relatively close to body.

NO

Slumped down into seat, back is rounded into seat, chin is dropped, arm is too far away from the body. This puts excessive pressure on the lower back.

Lifting golf bag and other heavy objects -

YES   **NO**

Standing close to the object you are lifting, bend your knees, keep your back straight and use your legs to provide the power to lift. This will reduce the stress placed on the lower back.

Standing too far away from the object, knees and arms in locked position. This position puts too much strain on the lower back and neck.

POSTURE

Many golfers are not aware of the importance of good posture. From the setup, through the backswing, and all the way to follow-through, good posture and balance throughout the swing will maximize power, control, and reduce the chance of golf-related injury. In addition, proper posture will allow the golfer to utilize each muscle during the swing, in the proper sequence, to its fullest potential.

Think of good posture this way — in the address position, if you were to draw a straight line from head to toe, it would travel directly through your earlobe, middle shoulder, middle knees, and the center of the ankle, respectively. Weight distribution is then balanced and provides for optimum swing mechanics, control, and power.

When Injury Occurs

Consider for a moment that the speed of the clubhead can reach upwards of 100 miles per hour in a well-executed drive, with these forces being repeated up to 150-300 times or more during a typical day of golf. Your body must be adequately prepared to handle this kind of constant force. However, even when a golfer engages in regular exercise, injuries inevitably occur.

For musculoskeletal injury (injury to muscles, tendons, ligaments, or bones), the RICE method (*rest, ice, compression, elevation*) as treatment can often be applied. This procedure is described here:

> **R**est the injured area
> **I**ce - apply ice for 20-30 minutes each hour for the
>   first 24 hours
> **C**ompression - wrapping the injured area with
>   elastic bandage can help to prevent
>   excessive swelling and speed recovery
> **E**levation - raising the injured area as high as
>   comfortably possible above the level of the heart

In most cases, golfing injuries won't sideline you for very long. Be patient and follow the advice of your doctor, who will give you clearance to resume play. When an injury does occur, stop play immediately and consult with your physician. Always listen to your body when you are playing golf - your body will tell you when something is wrong. That's the surest way to prevent golf-related injury.

While out on the course during play, it's a good idea to walk whenever possible. Try walking in-between your shots on occasion to keep your leg muscles loose and to keep the blood flowing to the working muscles. Remember also to wear comfortable golfing shoes to reduce the stresses placed upon your feet.

Taking the relatively small amount of time to exercise will greatly improve your chances of remaining injury-free. After all, isn't it worth a small amount of time to stay in good shape and avoid those nagging injuries, instead of being forced to exercise as a means of recovery? Exercise can not only improve your game, but it keeps you healthy and injury-free, playing the game you love for a lifetime.

(Note: The exercises mentioned in this chapter are designed to improve your conditioning and overall golfing posture. If you exhibit severe postural problems, seek the advice of a qualified sports medicine physician or physical therapist. They will help you regain proper form and function with a program developed according to your unique and specific needs.)

CHAPTER Nine

Taking It To the Course
Pre-Round and On-the-Course Stretching

"In golf, as in life, you get out of it what you put into it."
-Sam Snead

Now that you have learned that exercising regularly can take your golf game to the next level, let's take a look at what you can do *on the golf course* to be better prepared, both physically and mentally, before you take your first swing at the golf ball.

This chapter will highlight 12 key stretches that you can perform **BEFORE** you swing your first club, whether you're on the first tee or the practice range. **Choose <u>six</u> of your favorite stretches (<u>three</u> from the lower body and <u>three</u> from the upper body).** Do them before you tee off or before you hit balls on the practice range (they take only 2-3 minutes to complete all six).

Before your rounds, taking the time to stretch will calm your nerves, helping you to better communicate with your body and getting you into the state of mind to play relaxed, controlled, and consistently. These stretches will also improve your overall flexibility and range of motion, allowing you to **P.U.M.P.!** — perform **u**p to your **m**aximum **p**otential!

After a couple weeks of **<u>consistently</u>** performing the 6 stretches you've chosen, try the other 6 stretches for a couple of weeks, then alternate among the stretches for best results.

You should also **stretch on the course** as time permits during your round, for example, when you are waiting for that foursome ahead of you to clear the green, when play is slow, or when you feel anxious or lethargic. During the round, regular stretching keeps you physically and mentally alert, enhancing your ability to play your best golf. After the round, stretching can help to relieve soreness, prevent injury, and hinder the accumulation of dangerous toxins in your body.

Unfortunately, many golfers don't take the necessary time to warm up and stretch their bodies. Many times, they get to the course with just minutes to spare and dash right out to the first tee, or maybe hit a quick bucket of balls. It's no wonder these golfers struggle with their game, never reach their true potential, and often become highly susceptible to injury. Don't make the same mistake. Be **prepared** to play your best golf!

STRETCHING GUIDELINES

⇨ Warm up your body for a couple of minutes prior to beginning the stretches (for example, walking or jogging in place, walking up and down a few flights of stairs, doing 10-15 jumping jacks, etc.). This increases the effectiveness of the stretches and reduces the chances of pulling a muscle.

⇨ For best results, stretch your larger muscles first (such as the legs, hips, and back). Perform these stretches in this chapter in the order they are given (Stretch #1, followed by #2, #5, etc.).

⇨ Remember to hold each stretch for 10-15 seconds and breathe slowly and comfortably.

⇨ Perform each stretch at least once (if time permits, do them again).

⇨ Mentally relax and try to get in to the frame of mind of play — think of the types of shots you will be playing and confidently picture yourself playing great golf!

LOWER BODY

**Stretch #1: Quadriceps Stretch -
Target Area:** Thighs.

Standing tall, grasp your right ankle and gently pull that leg backwards and up until you feel a gentle stretch in the top of the thigh. Keep your knees pointed toward the ground. Hold 10-15 seconds. Repeat with the other leg. This stretch helps you generate power and maintain balance in your legs as you swing.

**Stretch #2: Standing Hip Flexor Stretch -
Target Area:** Front Hips.

You can do this stretch while you are tying your shoes, if you like. Stand upright next to a bench or golf cart with your legs shoulder width apart. Make sure that the right knee is directly over the right foot as you place your right foot on the cart or bench. Exhale as you lowly lean forward until a comfortable stretch is felt in the left front hip area and the back of the right leg. Hold 10-15 seconds. Repeat with the other side. This stretch will help you to transfer your weight and rotate into the ball with added power.

Stretch #3: Seated Hamstring Stretch -
Target Area: Hamstrings.

Sitting in a golf cart or on a comfortable bench, extend your right leg straight out on the seat with the left foot flat on the floor. Exhale as you slowly reach forward toward the right foot, as far as you can comfortably go. Keep your head up and avoid rounding your back. Try to feel the stretch in the hamstring area. Hold 10-15 seconds. Turn around and repeat with the left leg. This stretch is important for maintaining power in your legs and preventing lower back injuries.

Stretch #4: Calf Stretch -
Target Area: Calves

Note: This picture illustrates the stretch as performed on a standing calf raise machine, but you can use the edge of a step, golf cart, stair, etc. You may use one or both feet during this stretch. Allow your heel(s) to drop down as far as possible, while resting on the balls of your feet. Feel the stretch in your calf muscles and hold for a count of 10-15 seconds. This stretch will help to relieve muscular tension in your lower legs and improve balance and control throughout the swing.

Stretch #5: Lower Back Stretch-
Target Area: Back and shoulders.

Reach forward to grasp the side handles of a golf cart with your arms shoulder-width apart. With your feet flat on the ground, stick your buttocks back and bend your knees and chest toward the ground until you feel a comfortable stretch in the back, buttocks, and hips. Exhale to deeply feel this stretch. Hold for 10-15 seconds. To stretch the outer hips, allow your buttocks and hips to move slightly to the right or left while holding for 10-15 seconds.

Stretch #6: Trunk Rotation
Target Area: Trunk, abdominals, hips.

Using your golf club, bend your knees slightly and place the club behind your head and shoulders. Slowly rotate your upper body to one side, keeping your pelvis stationary and facing front, until you feel a comfortable stretch in the side abdomen. Exhale and hold for 5 seconds. Repeat to other side. Do 3 times to each side. Try to gradually increase the rotation a little bit with each repetition. This stretch gives you greater range-of-motion in your trunk, allowing you to generate more power and takes stress off the lower back during the swing.

115

UPPER BODY

Stretch #7: Chest Stretch-
Target Area: Chest, shoulders,biceps.

Hold a golf club behind your back with your hands slightly less than shoulder-width apart, palms facing up. Raise your arms and stick your chest out while trying to squeeze your shoulder blades together. Inhale deeply to achieve a full stretch in the chest. Hold 10-15 seconds. This stretch provides for better range-of-motion in the chest and shoulders during the swing for better control.

Stretch #8: Shoulder Stretch -
Target Area: Shoulders.

Standing or seated, reach across your body and under the right elbow, as shown. Grasp the back of your right elbow with your left hand and gently pull that arm across your body and under your chin until you feel a comfortable stretch in the shoulder region. Exhale and hold for 10-15 seconds. This stretch helps provide greater range-of-motion in the shoulders for a smoother and more controlled backswing and extended follow-through.

Stretch #9: Rotator Cuff Stretch
Target Area: Rotator cuff muscles in the upper back and shoulders.

Start

In a standing or seated position, place your knuckles against your temples as shown with your thumbs pointed down, elbows pushed back. Attempt to bring your elbows together in front of you, but don't force them together. Keep your head stationary and your knuckles pressed against your temples. Feel the stretch and release of tension in your upper back and back of your shoulders as you attempt to touch

Finish

your elbows together. Exhale slowly as you hold for 5 seconds. Return to the starting position, pushing your elbows back and squeezing your shoulder blades together. Hold 5 seconds. Do 3 times. This stretch helps your upper back muscles relax and allows freer movement in that area during the swing.

Stretch #10: Triceps Stretch - Target Area: Back of arms and shoulders.

Standing or seated in an upright position, raise your right arm over your head and bend the elbow until your right hand travels behind your head. Grasp the right elbow with your left hand and carefully bring your elbow up and toward the back of your head until a gentle stretch is felt in the back of the right arm near the right shoulder. Exhale slowly. Hold for 10-15 seconds. Repeat with the left arm. This stretch helps your arms maintain full extension during the swing, adding needed power and control.

Stretch #11: Neck Rotation Stretch - Target Area: Neck rotator muscles.

Keeping your shoulders facing forward, turn your head to one side (as if you are looking over your shoulder). Place your fingers against your chin and gently apply pressure until you feel a stretch along the side of the neck. Hold 10-15 seconds. Repeat to the other side. This stretch helps to relax the neck muscles and improves your ability to maintain a stationary head position as your shoulder rotate around the neck during the swing.

Stretch #12: Forearm Flexor Stretch - Target Area: Forearm flexor muscles.

Standing or seated in an upright position, extend your arm straight out in front of you at shoulder level. Using your other hand, gently pull the fingers of the extended hand upwards and backwards until a comfortable stretch is felt in the forearm. Hold for 10-15 seconds. Repeat with the other arm. This stretch increases your sense of grip pressure, allowing you to grip your club and increasing your ability to maintain better control over the club head.

Well, there you have it. In this book, I've put together some simple, convenient, and informative exercise techniques, nutritional tips, and tools to keep you motivated! As you begin to take the time to perform these exercises and techniques, they will feel as natural as swinging a golf club. Before you know it, you will be playing better, feeling better, and looking better; as your golfing performance improves, you'll have much more fun!

I hope you have enjoyed the process of learning about how to become a healthier golfer. It is my wish that you will be empowered to achieve your goals and reach for the best that is within you. Be patient, be honest with your efforts and **you will** become a healthier and better golfer. And remember, being in great shape will not only improve your golf game, but it can add years to your life and greatly enhance the quality of your life!

Good luck!

GOALS CHART

Short-term Goals:

Goals	Why Am I Committed?	Time Frame	Method
Work out 3 days per week on a golf fitness program	To feel better, have more energy, improve my flexibility, increase my club headcontrol, add 20 yards to my drives	1-2 months	Weights, stretching, aerobics
Lose 2 pounds per week	To look better and feel better	1-2 weeks	Exercise min. 3 days/wk
Eat more healthy foods	To have more energy, to increase my stamina	2-4 weeks	Start a food diary
Take golf lessons	To develop better swing mechanics	2-3 months	Visit golf pro
Spending 1 hour per week on golfing skills, bunker play, putting, irons	To improve my overall golf skills, to play more competitively	2-3 months	Visit local practice facility

Long-term Goals:

Goals	Why Am I Committed?	Time Frame	Method
Lower my blood pressure	To reduce my risk for heart problems	1 year & up	regular exercise lower stress
Better golf scores	To increase my enjoyment of golfing	6 months	consistent practice, exercise
Lose 20 pounds	To look better, to have more energy	3-6 months	exercise, eating right
Healthier lifestyle	For more enjoyment & time with family, friends	6 months	exercise, eating right, reduce my stress
Be a role model a fitness lifestyle	To help others adopt	1 year & up (practice what I preach)	be consistent
Quit smoking	To live a longer and healthier life	1-2 years & up	exercise, see my doctor

APPENDIX B:
FOOD DIARY

y/Meal	Meal	Snack	Meal	Snack	Meal	Snack	Daily Thoughts
nday							
sday							
dnesday							
rsday							
ay							
rday							
day							

*Overall weekly dietary notes (golf performance results/scores?
Were dietary goals met? Attitude/motivation level?):*

Thoughts/goals for upcoming week:

Use this diary as a guide in developing your own diary!

Weekly Exercise Journal

Week	Weight Training	Flexibility Training	Aerobic Training	Golfing Results	Daily Thoughts
Monday					
Tuesday					
Wednesday					
Thursday					
Friday					
Saturday					
Sunday					

WEEKLY NOTES

POSITIVE ASPECTS:

NEGATIVE ASPECTS:

*Use this journal as a guide in developing your own journal!

"Power Snack" Recipes

Here are a few of my favorite easy-to-prepare "power snack" recipes that you can eat during a round of golf (or anytime for that matter). They will help to provide you with the energy you need to stay physically and mentally sharp on and off the golf course. Share them with your family and friends!

Trail Mix-

1 cup unsalted, dry-roasted peanuts
1 cup unsalted, dry-roasted sunflower kernels or pumpkin seeds
2 cups raisins

Mix all ingredients together and bag in 1/4 cup portions.
Makes 16 servings.

Date Bars-

1 cup whole wheat pastry flour
1/2 cup wheat germ
1 teaspoon baking powder
2 teaspoons ground cinnamon
1/4 teaspoon ground allspice
1 cup unsweetened pitted dates, chopped
1/2 cup walnuts, chopped
3 eggs, beaten
1/3 cup honey
1 cup skim milk
1 teaspoon vanilla
nonstick cooking spray

Preheat oven to 350 degrees. Combine flour, wheat germ, baking powder, cinnamon, allspice, dates and walnuts in a medium-sized bowl; set aside. Mix the eggs, honey, milk and vanilla in a medium-sized bowl. Fold in the dry ingredients. Spread the batter in a 9 x 13-inch baking pan coated with nonstick cooking spray. Bake for about 20 minutes until golden brown. Makes 24 bars.

Apple Date Muffins-

1-1/2 cups Shredded Wheat N' Bran cereal
1-1/2 cups whole wheat pastry flour
1 tablespoon baking powder
1/2 teaspoon salt
1/2 teaspoon ground cinnamon
1/2 teaspoon apple pie spice
3 tablespoons canola oil
1/4 cup honey
1 egg
1 cup skim milk
1 cup unsweetened pitted dates, chopped

Finely process cereal in a blender or food processor. Mix with flour, baking powder, salt, cinnamon and apple pie spice; set aside. In a separate bowl beat oil, honey and egg until well blended. Add milk. Add flour mixture and stir until well blended; fold in dates and apples. Coat a muffin pan with nonstick cooking spray or line with paper muffin cups; fill each cup 2/3 full. Sprinkle top with dash of cinnamon. Bake for 25 minutes or until toothpick inserted in center comes out clean. Cool in pan on wire rack for 10 minutes; remove from pan and cool completely. Makes 16 muffins.

Raisin Bread-

2 tablespoons yeast (2 packages)
drop of honey
3 1/2 cups lukewarm water
1 1/2 teaspoons salt
1 tablespoon ground cinnamon
1/2 teaspoon ground ginger
2 tablespoons canola oil
2 tablespoons honey
1 1/2 cups raisins
9 cups whole wheat flour
nonstick cooking spray

Preheat oven to 350 degrees. In a large bowl dissolve the yeast and a drop of honey in 1/2 cup of the warm water until it "comes alive." Add salt, cinnamon and ginger; stir well. Stir in the remaining 3 cups water, oil, 2 tablespoons honey and raisins. Add 4 cups of flour and stir until well blended. Add the remaining flour 1 cup at a time until too thick to stir. Turn dough out onto a lightly floured board and continue to knead in more flour until dough is smooth and elastic (indentation from a finger poking will bounce back). Divide dough into 3 portions; form each portion into a loaf. Place each loaf in a small (7-7/8 x 3-7/8 inch) loaf pan coated with nonstick cooking spray. Allow dough to rise in uncovered pans until doubled in bulk. This bread will only rise once. Bake for 50 minutes until brown and hollow-sounding when tapped. Makes 3 loaves with 16 slices per loaf.

Cheese Apple Slices-

1 slice whole wheat bread
1/2 apple, thinly sliced
1 tablespoon raisins
1 ounce part-skim or nonfat mozzarella cheese

Preheat oven to broil. Top bread slice with apple slices and raisins. Place cheese on top of apple-raisin layer. Broil until cheese is bubbly. Makes 1 serving.

Homemade Granola-

4 cups old-fashioned oats, uncooked
3/4 cups unprocessed wheat bran
1/2 cup whole wheat pastry flour
2 cups wheat germ
1/2 cup oat bran
1/4 cup canola oil
2 tablespoons honey (optional)
1 cup sunflower kernels
1 cup raisins
2 teaspoons vanilla

Preheat oven to 300 degrees. Mix together oats, wheat bran, flour, wheat germ, oat bran, oil and honey. Spread into a large, shallow pan. Bake for 45 minutes, stirring every 15 minutes. Add the sunflower kernels during the last 10 minutes of baking. Add the raisins and vanilla at the end of the baking time. Let cool. Makes 42 servings.

Pita Pizzas-

1 whole wheat pita, cut in half into rounds (like a Frisbee)
2 tablespoons spaghetti sauce
2 ounces part-skim or nonfat mozzarella cheese, shredded

Preheat oven to 375 degrees. Place the two pita circles on a baking sheet. Spread each with half of the spaghetti sauce and top each with half of the cheese. Bake for 8 to 10 minutes or until cheese is bubbly. Makes 1 serving.

Healthy Grilled Cheese

2 slices whole wheat bread
2 ounces part-skim or low-fat cheddar cheese, sliced
apple or tomato slices (optional)
nonstick cooking spray

Coat a skillet with nonstick cooking spray. Place 1 slice of bread in skillet; top with cheese and a few apple or tomato slices, if desired. Top with the other slice of bread. Grill sandwich on both sides until bread is lightly browned and cheese is melted. Makes 1 serving.

(These recipes were reprinted with permission from the book
"Eat Well, Live Well - The Nutrition Guide and Cookbook for Healthy, Productive Living"
by Pamela M. Smith, RD.)

References/Suggested Readings

Carpenter, S.M., & F.P. Kendall. 1995. *Golfers Take Care of Your Back.* Vestal, NY: Thistle Ridge Press.

Cotton, Richard T. 1996. *Personal Trainer Manual.* San Diego, CA: American Council on Exercise.

Covey, Stephen R., A. Roger Merrill, Rebecca Merrill. 1994. *First Things First.* New York, NY: Simon & Schuster.

Jobe, F., Robert E. Mottram, Marilyn M. Pink, Lewis A. Yocum. 1994. *Exercise Guide to Better Golf.* Champaign, IL: Human Kinetics.

Myers, Randy M.LS. 1996. *The Official PGA National Golf Stretching Guide.* West Palm Beach, FL: Cart One Corporation.

Player, Gary. 1995. Fit for Golf. New York, NY: Simon & Schuster.

Robbins, Anthony. 1986. *Unlimited Power.* New York, NY: Simon & Schuster.

Tinder, Don. 1998. "Group Exercise Classes for Golfers." *IDEA Health & Fitness Source* May: 27-32.

Tinder, Don. 1998. "Golfing Fitness." *Fitness Plus* May: 30-34, 86.

Tinder, Don. 1998. "How To Prevent A Bad Back." *Golf Illustrated* May/June: 18-19.

Tinder, Don. 1998. "Muscle Your Way to A Better Game." *New Man* May: 46-47.

Tinder, Don. 1998. "What's Your Golf Fitness IQ?" *Golf Illustrated* January/February: 17-18.

Other Books from New Century Publishers 2000

A Doctor in your Suitcase by Dr. Michael Gazsi, N.D. and Nina Anderson, S.P.N.
$7.95 US $11.95 CA
A quick reference pocket guide to nutritional, herbal, homeopathic treatments and folk remedies to heal common illnesses we face while away-from-home.

Velvet Antler, Nature's Superior Tonic by Alison Davidson
$9.95 US $14.95 CA
Amazing health breakthroughs from this powerful rejuvenating tonic.

Self-Care Anywhere by Gary Skole, Scott Greenberg, M.D., Michael Gazsi, N.D.
$19.95 US $29.95 CA
Integrated self-help remedies combining the best conventional medicine, herbal, nutritional, homeopathic and mind/body. Teaching you how to take control of your health.

Plant Power *Revised* by Laurel Dewey
$19.95 US $29.95 CA
The Humorous Herbalist's guide to finding, growing, gathering & using 30 great medicinal herbs.

TO ORDER CALL (877) 742-7078 (credit cards accepted)
Please add $3.00 shipping for titles under $10.00,
$4.00 shipping for all titles over $10.00.

TO ORDER BY MAIL: Send check to:
Fenwick Communications
60 Bullock Drive, Unit 6
Markham, ON L3P 3P2